BIOLOGY

· PRINCIPLES & EXPLORATIONS ·

Chapter Tests
with Answer Key

HOLT, RINEHART AND WINSTON

A Harcourt Classroom Education Company

Austin · New York · Orlando · Atlanta · San Francisco · Boston · Dallas · Toronto · London

Illustration Credits: Page 1, Rosiland Solomon; 6, Kristy Sprott; 11, David Kelley; 65, David Kelley; 71, Morgan-Cain & Associates; 72, Rosiland Solomon; 92, David Kelley; 95, David Kelley; 104, David Kelley; 113, David Kelley.

Printed in the United States of America

ISBN 0-03-054359-2

3 4 5 6 7 8 9   18   05 04 03 02 01

Table of Contents

Name _____ Date _____ Class _____

Biology and You

Questions 1–5 refer to the figures below, which show cheetahs and a paramecium.

 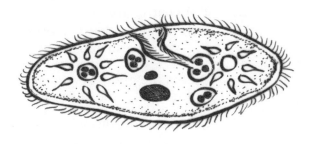

Circle T *if the statement is true or* F *if it is false.*

T   F   **1.** Reproduction ensures the ongoing success of both species.

T   F   **2.** Both species are multicellular.

T   F   **3.** Unlike the cheetahs, the paramecium does not have to maintain a stable internal environment.

T   F   **4.** Both the cheetahs and the paramecium exhibit organization.

T   F   **5.** Both species have DNA in their cells.

In the space provided, write the letter of the term or phrase that best completes each statement or best answers each question.

_____   **6.** Which of the following is NOT a reason to study the rain forest?
  a. to understand how to balance the needs of plants, animals, and people
  b. to find cures for diseases
  c. to learn how to clear the forest of trees quickly
  d. to save many of the world's plant and animal species

_____   **7.** Scientists usually design experiments
  a. with a good idea of how the experiments are going to come out.
  b. based upon wild guesses.
  c. to learn how to use new laboratory tools.
  d. All of the above

_____   **8.** A unifying explanation for a broad range of observations is a
  a. hypothesis.
  b. theory.
  c. prediction.
  d. controlled experiment.

_____ 9. Generally, the stages of a scientific investigation proceed in the following order:

   a. observations, predictions, hypothesis, verifying predictions, theory, verification.
   b. observations, hypothesis, making predictions, testing predictions with experiments, theory.
   c. predictions, observations, hypothesis, theory, controlled testing, verification.
   d. observations, hypothesis, predictions, verification, theory.

_____ 10. A control group

   a. requires a lead scientist who controls a group of scientists conducting an experiment.
   b. is always registered with the Food and Drug Administration (FDA).
   c. is the group in an experiment that receives no experimental treatment.
   d. provides the answer to a problem posed by a theory.

_____ 11. A theory, in the scientific sense, is

   a. the same as a hypothesis.
   b. an uncertain guess.
   c. a set of tested and confirmed related hypotheses.
   d. a prediction.

_____ 12. Biologist John Harte wanted to determine why there was a decline in the number of salamanders. Based on his observations, Harte suggested that acid rain might be responsible. This suggestion was a

   a. prediction.
   b. hypothesis.
   c. theory.
   d. scientific "truth."

_____ 13. Harte thought that the acid released by melting snow each spring would kill the salamanders. This idea was a

   a. prediction.
   b. hypothesis.
   c. theory.
   d. scientific "truth."

_____ 14. In order to produce more food, scientists are looking for ways to develop crops that

   a. will grow more efficiently in tropical soils.
   b. will grow without extensive use of fertilizers and pesticides.
   c. are more resistant to insects.
   d. All of the above

_____ 15. AIDS is caused by

   a. a defective gene in the immune system.
   b. the human immunodeficiency virus (HIV).
   c. a bacterium.
   d. All of the above

Name _____ Date _____ Class _____

Complete each statement by writing the correct term or phrase in the space provided.

16. A(n) _____ is the smallest unit capable of all life functions.

17. _____ is the transfer of genetic traits from parent to offspring.

18. All living things require _____ to run the processes of life.

19. All living things maintain a balance within their cells and the environment

   through the process of _____ .

20. Parents produce offspring through _____ .

21. Molecules of _____ encode information to direct the growth and development of cells.

22. A possible cure for cystic fibrosis uses a technique called

   _____ _____ .

23. Diet, exposure to chemicals, and tobacco use can all affect a person's chances

   of developing _____ .

Read each question, and write your answer in the space provided.

24. Some scientists think that increased exposure to ultraviolet (UV) radiation is harming amphibian populations. Write a hypothesis and a prediction stating that UV radiation is harmful to amphibians. Then design an experiment to test your hypothesis. What previous data and observations must be known in order to design the experiment?

   _____

   _____

   _____

   _____

   _____

25. If the results of an experiment do not support the hypothesis that the experiment was designed to test, was the experiment a waste of time? Explain.

   _____

   _____

   _____

   _____

   _____

CHAPTER

2 **TEST**

Chemistry of Life

Circle T *if the statement is true or* F *if it is false.*

T F **1.** Activation energy is needed only by chemical reactions that release energy.

T F **2.** In ions, the number of protons is equal to the number of electrons.

T F **3.** A solution is a mixture of unevenly distributed substances.

T F **4.** Polar substances dissolve well in water, which is also polar.

T F **5.** All the chemical reactions within an organism are referred to as metabolism.

In the space provided, write the letter of the term or phrase that best completes each statement or best answers each question.

_____ **6.** Atoms contain

    a. protons.
    b. electrons.
    c. neutrons.
    d. All of the above

_____ **7.** The bonds between water molecules are called

    a. covalent bonds.
    b. hydrogen bonds.
    c. ionic and covalent bonds.
    d. covalent and hydrogen bonds.

_____ **8.** An atom is called an ion when it has

    a. either lost or gained electrons.
    b. either lost or gained protons.
    c. more neutrons than protons.
    d. lost its nucleus.

_____ **9.** The ability of water to form drops is an example of

    a. capillary action.
    b. cohesion.
    c. adhesion.
    d. ionic bonding.

_____ **10.** Two solutions, A and B, are tested for pH. Solution A indicates a pH of 2. Solution B indicates a pH of 7. You conclude that

    a. both solutions are acidic.
    b. solution A is basic; solution B is neutral.
    c. solution A is acidic; solution B is neutral.
    d. None of the above

_____ **11.** Glycogen and starch
   a. are made of a sugar, a base, and a phosphate group.
   b. can be either saturated or unsaturated.
   c. are made of amino acids.
   d. are carbohydrates in which energy is stored.

_____ **12.** Enzymes
   a. are usually proteins.
   b. increase the speed of chemical reactions.
   c. reduce the activation energy of chemical reactions.
   d. All of the above

Questions 13–15 refer to the chemical reaction shown in the equation below.

$$NaCl \longrightarrow Na^+ + Cl^-$$

Complete each statement by writing the correct term or phrase in the space provided.

13. In the chemical reaction shown above, sodium chloride is the

_____ , and sodium ions and chloride ions are the

_____ .

14. In this chemical reaction, the type of chemical bonds being broken are

_____ bonds.

15. Salt dissolves in water because it is _____ . Oil, a(n)

_____ substance, does not dissolve in water.

16. Carbon dioxide, oxygen gas, and water are all examples

of _____ .

17. A solution containing water and lime juice would be _____ .

18. An enzyme acts only on specific _____ , which attach to

the enzyme's _____ _____ .

19. _____ is the main energy currency of cells.

20. Single sugars, called _____ , supply

_____ to cells.

21. Enzymes help organisms maintain _____ , a stable internal
condition.

Name_____ Date _____ Class _____

Questions 22 and 23 refer to the figure below.

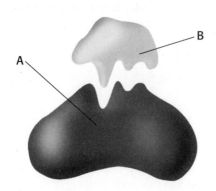

Read each question, and write your answer in the space provided.

22. Identify the structures labeled *A* and *B*.

_____

_____

23. How does the structure labeled *A* increase the speed of a chemical reaction?

_____

_____

_____

_____

24. Briefly describe the structures of proteins, nucleic acids, and nucleotides.

_____

_____

_____

_____

_____

_____

25. Describe the locations of the covalent and hydrogen bonds in a drop of water.

_____

_____

_____

_____

CHAPTER

3 **TEST**

Cell Structure

Circle T *if the statement is true or* F *if it is false.*

T   F   **1.** Small cells can transport materials and information more quickly than larger cells can.

T   F   **2.** Newly made proteins are transported to the smooth endoplasmic reticulum for further processing.

T   F   **3.** Scanning electron microscopes can be used to view only nonliving specimens.

T   F   **4.** A nanometer (nm) is smaller than a micrometer (μm).

T   F   **5.** In plants, chloroplasts use light energy to make carbohydrates from carbon dioxide and water.

In the space provided, write the letter of the term or phrase that best completes each statement or best answers each question.

_____ **6.** Which of the following is one difference between prokaryotes and eukaryotes?
   a. Nucleic acids are found only in prokaryotes.
   b. Eukaryotes contain mitochondria.
   c. Organelles are found only in prokaryotes.
   d. Prokaryotes have a nuclear membrane.

_____ **7.** An example of a prokaryotic cell is a(n)
   a. animal cell.   **c.** bacterium.
   b. plant cell.   **d.** None of the above

_____ **8.** The nucleus of a cell contains all of the following EXCEPT
   a. chromosomes.   **c.** DNA.
   b. mitochondria.   **d.** RNA.

_____ **9.** Which type of molecule is found in the cell membrane?
   a. carbohydrate   **c.** phospholipid
   b. protein   **d.** all of the above

_____ **10.** The interior of a cell is called the
   a. cytoplasm.   **c.** flagellum.
   b. cytoskeleton.   **d.** cilium.

_____ **11.** The lipid bilayer of the cell membrane
   a. provides a boundary between the cell and its surroundings.
   b. forms vesicles.
   c. transports substances into and out of the cell.
   d. All of the above

_____ 12. Which of the following types of microscopes can be used to view living specimens?

    a. transmission electron microscope
    b. scanning electron microscope
    c. light microscope
    d. none of the above

_____ 13. A cell's digestive enzymes are stored in

    a. Golgi apparatus.   **c.** ribosomes.
    b. lysosomes.   **d.** mitochondria.

Questions 14–16 refer to the figure below, which shows the packaging and distribution of proteins inside the cell.

_____ 14. The structures labeled *A* are

    a. vesicles.   **c.** ribosomes.
    b. lysosomes.   **d.** chloroplasts.

_____ 15. The structure labeled *B* is

    a. the endoplasmic reticulum.   **c.** a mitochondrion.
    b. a Golgi apparatus.   **d.** the nucleus.

_____ 16. The structure labeled *D* is a(n)

    a. mitochondrion.   **c.** ribosome.
    b. endoplasmic reticulum.   **d.** vesicle.

Complete each statement by writing the correct term or phrase in the space provided.

17. The statement "Cells arise only from existing cells" is part of the

_____ _____ .

18. Proteins remain embedded in the lipid bilayer because some amino acids are

_____ , as is the interior of the lipid bilayer.

19. _____ and _____ are structures that enable cell movement and sometimes move substances across a cell's surface.

20. The meshlike network of microscopic protein fibers that supports the shape

of the cell is called the _____ .

21. In a light microscope, the _____ lens is closest to the eye, while

the _____ lens is closest to the specimen.

22. Ribosomes are found on the _____ endoplasmic reticulum.

Read each question, and write your answer in the space provided.

23. Why are mitochondria important to the functioning of eukaryotic cells?

_____

_____

_____

_____

24. Why are both magnification and resolution important in microscopes?

_____

_____

_____

_____

25. Describe the four kinds of proteins that are embedded in the cell membrane.

_____

_____

_____

_____

_____

Name _____ Date _____ Class _____

Cells and Their Environment

Circle T *if the statement is true or* F *if it is false.*

T   F   **1.** The sodium-potassium pump transports potassium ions into the cell.

T   F   **2.** A cell placed in a hypertonic solution could burst.

T   F   **3.** The transport of a specific substance down its concentration gradient by a carrier protein is called facilitated diffusion.

T   F   **4.** Exocytosis helps a cell rid itself of wastes.

In the space provided, write the letter of the term or phrase that best completes each statement or best answers each question.

_____   **5.** Which type of membrane protein transmits information into the cell by responding to signal molecules?
   a. carrier protein   **c.** marker protein
   b. receptor protein   **d.** none of the above

_____   **6.** Which of the following is NOT a characteristic of active transport?
   a. It moves substances against a concentration gradient.
   b. It requires energy from the cell.
   c. It involves facilitated diffusion.
   d. It relies on carrier proteins that often function as pumps.

_____   **7.** Diffusion is the movement of a substance
   a. through only a lipid bilayer.
   b. from an area of low concentration to an area of higher concentration.
   c. only in liquids.
   d. from an area of high concentration to an area of lower concentration.

_____   **8.** If the concentration of a sugar solution is lower outside the cell than inside the cell, which of the following will happen by osmosis?
   a. Sugar will move into the cell.
   b. Water will move into the cell.
   c. Sugar will move out of the cell.
   d. Water will move out of the cell.

_____   **9.** An ion channel is a transport protein that
   a. moves substances against a concentration gradient.
   b. pumps ions only out of a cell.
   c. moves ions across the cell membrane so that the ions do not come in contact with the nonpolar interior of the lipid bilayer.
   d. has pores that are always open.

_____   **10.** Molecules that are too large to be moved through the cell membrane can be transported into the cell by
   a. osmosis.   **c.** exocytosis.
   b. endocytosis.   **d.** diffusion.

Name _____ Date _____ Class _____

Questions 11–14 refer to the figure below, which shows transport through the cell membrane.

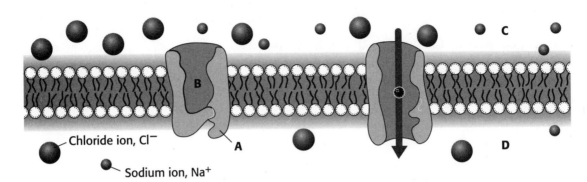

Chloride ion, Cl⁻

Sodium ion, Na⁺

_____ **11.** The structure labeled *A* is
   a. a gated ion channel.
   b. a sodium-potassium pump.
   c. an active transport protein.
   d. a messenger protein.

_____ **12.** The interior of the pore, labeled *B*, enables substances to pass through the cell membrane without coming in contact with
   a. the solution outside the cell.
   b. the nonpolar interior of the lipid bilayer.
   c. the polar interior of the lipid bilayer.
   d. All of the above

_____ **13.** Which area has the greatest concentration of ions in solution?
   a. *A*
   b. *B*
   c. *C*
   d. *D*

_____ **14.** What type of transport is illustrated by the figure above?
   a. osmosis
   b. active transport
   c. facilitated diffusion
   d. diffusion

Complete each statement by writing the correct term or phrase in the space provided.

15. A cell membrane is _____ permeable because it allows the passage of some substances and not others.

16. Using energy to transport molecules through a membrane from an area of low concentration to an area of higher concentration is called

_____ _____ .

17. In facilitated diffusion, _____ _____ move substances down their concentration gradient.

18. In _____ , substances outside a cell are transported into the cell by vesicles.

19. A(n) _____ _____ binds to a specific signal molecule, causing changes in the cell.

20. A cell shrinks when it is placed in a(n) _____ solution.

Read each question, and write your answer in the space provided.

21. Why is it dangerous for humans to drink sea water?

_____

_____

_____

22. Explain how the sodium-potassium pump works and why it is important.

_____

_____

_____

_____

_____

23. Describe three ways in which the binding of a signal molecule to a receptor protein can change the activities of the receiving cell.

_____

_____

_____

_____

24. Distinguish between diffusion and active transport.

_____

_____

_____

25. Describe how different kinds of cells react to hypertonic solutions.

_____

_____

_____

Name _____ Date _____ Class _____

Photosynthesis and Cellular Respiration

Circle T *if the statement is true or* F *if it is false.*

T   F   **1.** An autotroph is able to make organic compounds from light or from inorganic substances.

T   F   **2.** The light-independent reactions of photosynthesis can occur only in the dark.

T   F   **3.** Aerobic respiration must follow glycolysis if a cell is to maximize its ATP production.

T   F   **4.** The Calvin cycle is a common method of aerobic respiration.

In the space provided, write the letter of the term or phrase that best completes each statement or best answers each question.

_____   **5.** The energy a cell needs to build molecules or to power cellular respiration is supplied by
    a. electron transport chains.   **c.** water and ADP.
    b. ATP.   **d.** the Calvin cycle.

_____   **6.** Glycolysis yields
    a. two 6-carbon molecules.
    b. four NADH molecules.
    c. a large amount of ATP and NADH.
    d. two pyruvates, two NADH molecules, and four ATP molecules.

_____   **7.** When a chlorophyll molecule absorbs light,
    a. some of its electrons are excited to a higher energy level.
    b. it disintegrates.
    c. it absorbs mostly green light.
    d. it absorbs all wavelengths of light.

_____   **8.** When electrons of a chlorophyll molecule are excited to a higher energy level,
    a. they become ions.
    b. they are not excited.
    c. they enter an electron transport chain.
    d. carotenoids are converted to chlorophyll.

_____   **9.** The source of oxygen produced during photosynthesis is
    a. carbon dioxide.   **c.** air.
    b. water.   **d.** glucose.

_____   **10.** Which of the following is NOT part of cellular respiration?
    a. electron transport chain   **c.** Krebs cycle
    b. glycolysis   **d.** Calvin cycle

_____ 11. NADPH is formed when the electron acceptor NADP⁺ combines with

    a. hydrogen ions and excited electrons.
    b. excited electrons and ATP.
    c. hydrogen ions and glucose.
    d. excited electrons and proteins.

_____ 12. ATP releases energy when

    a. new phosphate groups are added.
    b. the 5-carbon sugar detaches.
    c. the bonds between phosphate groups are broken.
    d. the nitrogen-containing base breaks down.

_____ 13. In the Krebs cycle, production of ATP requires

    a. acetyl-CoA.
    b. the gradual breakdown of a 6-carbon compound.
    c. the transfer of a phosphate group to ADP.
    d. All of the above

Questions 14 and 15 refer to the figures below.

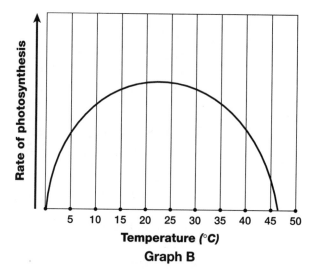

Effect of Light Intensity on Photosynthesis

Rate of photosynthesis

Increasing light intensity
Graph A

Effect of Temperature on Photosynthesis

Rate of photosynthesis

5 10 15 20 25 30 35 40 45 50

Temperature (°C)
Graph B

_____ 14. Graph A demonstrates that the rate of photosynthesis

    a. decreases in response to increasing light intensity.
    b. increases indefinitely in response to increasing light intensity.
    c. increases in response to increasing light intensity but only to a certain point.
    d. is not affected by changes in light intensity.

_____ 15. Taken together, these graphs demonstrate that

    a. photosynthesis is independent of environmental influences.
    b. increases in light intensity cause increases in temperature.
    c. as the rate of photosynthesis increases, the temperature eventually decreases.
    d. the rate of photosynthesis is affected by changes in the environment.

Name_____ Date _____ Class _____

Complete each statement by writing the correct term or phrase in the space provided.

16. The ultimate source of energy for all life on Earth is the

_____ .

17. Heterotrophs cannot get energy from the sun directly and rely on

_____ _____ to provide energy to function.

18. The _____ _____ begins when a molecule of carbon dioxide is added to a 5-carbon compound and ends with 3-carbon sugars.

19. During glycolysis, NADH is formed when hydrogen atoms are transferred to

an electron acceptor called _____ .

20. _____ serves as the final electron acceptor for the electron transport chain of aerobic respiration.

21. _____ use light energy or inorganic substances to produce organic compounds.

22. _____ converts light energy to chemical energy.

23. During photosynthesis, oxygen gas is produced when water molecules are split

to provide replacement _____ for pigment molecules.

Read each question, and write your answer in the space provided.

24. If the Calvin cycle uses carbon dioxide, not light energy, to make organic compounds, explain why it cannot be the first stage of photosynthesis.

_____

_____

_____

_____

25. In order for pyruvate to be used for the production of ATP, oxygen must be present. What happens to pyruvate produced during glycolysis if oxygen is not available to a cell?

_____

_____

_____

_____

Name_____ Date _____ Class_____

CHAPTER

6 **TEST**

Chromosomes and Cell Reproduction

Circle T *if the statement is true or* F *if it is false.*

T   F   **1.** The information a cell needs to direct its activities and to determine its characteristics is contained in molecules of deoxyribonucleic acid (DNA).

T   F   **2.** Each human somatic cell contains 2 copies of each chromosome for a total of 23 homologous chromosomes.

T   F   **3.** Gametes are diploid so that when fertilization occurs, the resulting zygote will have the characteristic number of chromosomes for the species.

T   F   **4.** Autosomes determine the sex of an individual.

T   F   **5.** During cytokinesis, a cell's cytoplasm divides.

In the space provided, write the letter of the term or phrase that best completes each statement or best answers each question.

_____   **6.** Chromatids are

        a. tightly coiled DNA.
        b. bacterial chromosomes.
        c. strands of duplicate genetic material.
        d. supercoils of protein.

_____   **7.** If conditions are favorable for cell division during the G_1 phase,

        a. the microtubules attach to the centromeres.
        b. the nucleus begins to divide.
        c. the centriole pair is replicated.
        d. proteins stimulate the cell to copy its DNA.

_____   **8.** A student can study a karyotype to learn about the

        a. process of binary fission.
        b. genes that are present in a particular strand of DNA.
        c. medical history of an individual.
        d. chromosomes present in the somatic cell.

_____   **9.** If nondisjunction occurs,

        a. too many gametes will be produced.
        b. no gametes will be produced.
        c. a gamete will receive too many or too few homologues of a chromosome.
        d. a mutation occurs.

_____   **10.** The stage of the cell cycle that occupies most of the cell's life is

        a. G_1.
        b. M.
        c. G_2.
        d. S.

Copyright © by Holt, Rinehart and Winston. All rights reserved.

_____ **11.** Spindles are composed of
   a. nine triplets of microtubules.
   b. individual microtubule fibers and centrioles.
   c. chromatids and centromeres.
   d. microtubules arranged in a circle around the centriole.

Questions 12 and 13 refer to the figure below, which shows the stages of mitosis.

A   **B**   **C**   **D**

_____ **12.** Which of the following correctly indicates the order in which mitosis occurs?
   a. *A, B, C, D*
   b. *B, A, C, D*
   c. *C, B, A, D*
   d. *A, C, B, D*

_____ **13.** Which stage shows metaphase?
   a. *A*
   b. *B*
   c. *C*
   d. *D*

Complete each statement by writing the correct term or phrase in the space provided.

14. A fertilized egg cell is called a(n) _____ .

15. _____ _____ is the process by which a bacterial cell splits asexually into two identical organisms.

16. Collectively, the time spent in G_1, S, and G_2 is called _____ .

17. A zygote is formed by the union of two haploid _____ from the opposite sexes.

18. During cell division, the movement of chromosomes is aided by a structure

called the _____ .

19. Cancer can occur when _____ mutate and the

_____ that regulate cell growth and division do not function.

20. _____ _____ are similar in shape, size, and genetic content.

21. A DNA molecule contains thousands of _____ , and the DNA

   and its associated proteins form _____ .

22. If a piece of a chromosome breaks off, a(n) _____

   _____ occurs.

Read each question, and write your answer in the space provided.

23. Describe how a karyotype can be used to diagnose Down syndrome.

   _____

   _____

   _____

   _____

   _____

   _____

24. Briefly describe the five stages of the cell cycle.

   _____

   _____

   _____

   _____

   _____

   _____

25. Describe the difference between cytokinesis in animal cells and plant cells.

   _____

   _____

   _____

   _____

   _____

   _____

   _____

CHAPTER
7 **TEST**

Meiosis and Sexual Reproduction

Circle T *if the statement is true or* F *if it is false.*

T F **1.** The chromosomes replicate again between meiosis I and meiosis II.

T F **2.** Fission produces genetically identical individuals of about equal size.

T F **3.** Oogenesis produces only one functional egg cell.

T F **4.** Meiosis results in the formation of haploid cells from diploid cells.

T F **5.** Cytokinesis only occurs during metaphase II.

In the space provided, write the letter of the term or phrase that best completes each statement or best answers each question.

_____ **6.** Meiosis occurs
    a. in all sexually reproducing organisms.
    b. in all asexually reproducing organisms.
    c. in all reproducing organisms.
    d. during gametogenesis and cytokinesis.

_____ **7.** Which of the following is NOT affected by genetic variation?
    a. the development of improved animal breeds
    b. the pace of evolution
    c. the ability of organisms to adapt to changing conditions
    d. the frequency of reproduction

Questions 8 and 9 refer to the figure below, which shows the stages of meiosis.

    A   **B**   **C**   **D**

_____ **8.** Pairs of homologous chromosomes line up at the cell's equator in stage
    a. *A.*
    b. *B.*
    c. *C.*
    d. *D.*

_____ **9.** Homologous chromosomes move to opposite poles of the cell during stage
    a. *A.*
    b. *B.*
    c. *C.*
    d. *D.*

_____ **10.** In alternation of generations, which of the following is NOT haploid?
    a. spores
    b. gametophytes
    c. sporophytes
    d. eggs and sperm

_____ **11.** During meiosis, two successive divisions
    a. result in the formation of two identical cells.
    b. cause the formation of a zygote.
    c. are responsible for the formation of four haploid cells.
    d. must occur before mitosis can form gametes.

_____ **12.** In asexual reproduction,
    a. DNA does not vary much between offspring.
    b. many offspring are produced in a short time.
    c. organisms may not be able to adapt to new environments.
    d. All of the above

_____ **13.** Fragmentation is a form of
    a. fission.
    b. asexual reproduction.
    c. crossing-over.
    d. sexual reproduction.

_____ **14.** In humans, each gamete receives
    a. 23 pairs of chromosomes from each parent.
    b. one chromosome from each of 23 pairs.
    c. 46 chromosomes.
    d. 23 homologous chromosomes.

Complete each statement by writing the correct term or phrase in the space provided.

15. The final cells resulting from meiosis in either males or females are called

_____ .

16. The chromatids remain attached at their centromeres until

_____ .

17. In alternation of generations, spores are produced by the process of

_____ , and gametes are produced by the process of

_____ .

18. Sexual reproduction may have its origins in the formation of

_____ _____ by protists, which allowed

the repair of damaged _____ .

19. _____ _____ contributes to the evolution
of organisms.

20. The process called _____ guarantees that the number of chromosomes in gametes is half the number of chromosomes in body cells.

21. Offspring that result from _____ _____ resemble, but are not identical to, their parents because of

_____ _____ .

22. If the gametes of an individual are its only haploid cells, that individual has

a(n) _____ life cycle.

Read each question, and write your answer in the space provided.

23. Explain why crossing-over is an important source of genetic variation.

_____

_____

_____

_____

24. Explain how independent assortment and crossing-over can produce a practically unlimited number of genetic combinations among gametes.

_____

_____

_____

_____

25. What is a disadvantage of sexual reproduction?

_____

_____

_____

_____

CHAPTER

8 **TEST**

Mendel and Heredity

Circle T *if the statement is true or* F *if it is false.*

T F **1.** Gregor Mendel's heredity experiments were considered cutting edge for their time because of Mendel's quantitative approach.

T F **2.** Heterozygous individuals have two of the same alleles for a particular gene.

T F **3.** If a mutated piece of DNA is carried in a recessive allele, the only way for this mutated allele to be expressed in a child born to two unaffected parents would be for both parents to be heterozygous carriers of this mutated allele.

T F **4.** An autosomal trait will occur with equal frequency in both males and females.

In the space provided, write the letter of the term or phrase that best completes each statement or best answers each question.

_____ **5.** When two different alleles occur together, the one that is expressed is called

    a. dominant.   **c.** recessive.

    b. phenotypic.   **d.** superior.

_____ **6.** An organism that has inherited two of the same alleles of a gene from its parents is _____ for that trait.

    a. hereditary   **c.** homozygous

    b. heterozygous   **d.** a mutation

_____ **7.** The law of segregation states that

    a. alleles of a gene separate from each other during gamete formation.

    b. different alleles of a gene can never be found in the same organism.

    c. each gene of an organism ends up in a different gamete.

    d. each gene is found on a different molecule of DNA.

_____ **8.** The law of independent assortment applies only to genes that are

    a. sex-linked.

    b. located on different chromosomes or are far apart on the same chromosome.

    c. located on the same chromosome.

    d. autosomal.

_____ **9.** Both sickle cell anemia and hemophilia

    a. are caused by genes coding for defective proteins.

    b. are seen in homozygous dominant individuals.

    c. provide resistance to malaria infections.

    d. are extremely common throughout the world.

_____ 10. If a characteristic is sex-linked, it
  a. occurs most commonly in males.
  b. occurs only in females.
  c. can never occur in females.
  d. is always fatal.

_____ 11. Which of the following is an example of gene therapy?
  a. A genetic counselor studies a pedigree.
  b. A student studies the colors of flowers in pea plants.
  c. A geneticist explains the inheritance of albinism by using a Punnett square.
  d. A physician transfers a normal gene into the DNA of a person with a mutated form of the gene.

Questions 12–15 refer to the figure below, which shows a cross between two rabbits. In rabbits, black fur (B) is dominant to brown fur (b).

	B	b
B	1	2
b	3	4

$Bb \times Bb$

_____ 12. The device illustrated above, which is used to organize genetic analysis, is called a
  a. Mendelian box.   c. genetic graph.
  b. Punnett square.   d. phenotypic paradox.

_____ 13. The fur in both of the parents in the cross is
  a. black.   c. homozygous dominant.
  b. brown.   d. homozygous recessive.

_____ 14. The phenotype of the offspring indicated by Box 3 would be
  a. brown.
  b. a mixture of brown and black.
  c. black.
  d. The phenotype cannot be determined.

_____ 15. The genotype ratio ($BB : Bb$) of the F_1 generation would be
  a. 1:1.   c. 1:3.
  b. 3:1.   d. None of the above

Complete each statement by writing the correct term or phrase in the space provided.

16. When sperm and egg cells fuse during fertilization, the resulting offspring has two _____ for each trait.

17. When two members of the F_1 generation are crossed, the offspring are referred

    to as the _____ generation.

18. Different forms of a particular gene are called _____ .

19. The likelihood that a specific event will occur is called _____ .

20. Changes in genetic material are called _____ .

21. A trait that is determined by a gene found only on the X chromosome

    is said to be a(n) _____ _____ trait.

Read each question, and write your answer in the space provided.

22. Explain how polygenic traits occur.

    _____

    _____

    _____

    _____

23. Explain why sex-linked traits are more common in males than in females.

    _____

    _____

    _____

    _____

    _____

24. Give two examples of traits that are influenced by the environment.

    _____

    _____

    _____

25. Explain how the genetic disorder PKU can lead to mental retardation if it is
    not treated in infancy.

    _____

    _____

    _____

CHAPTER

9   TEST

DNA: The Genetic Material

Circle T *if the statement is true or* F *if it is false.*

T   F   **1.** Even though they contain inactivated or dead pathogens, vaccines still will cause an immune response when injected into an organism.

T   F   **2.** The strands of a DNA molecule are held together by hydrogen bonding between adenine and guanine molecules and cytosine and thymine molecules.

T   F   **3.** The work of Chargaff, Wilkins, and Franklin helped to define the shape and structure of DNA.

T   F   **4.** According to the base-pairing rules, an adenine on one strand always pairs with a thymine on the opposite strand, and a cytosine on one strand always pairs with guanine on the opposite strand.

In the space provided, write the letter of the term or phrase that best completes each statement or best answers each question.

_____   **5.** Oswald Avery and his co-workers demonstrated that treating bacteria with DNA-destroying enzymes
   a. also inactivated proteins in the cells.
   b. caused the bacteria to undergo transformation.
   c. prevented harmless bacteria from transforming into deadly bacteria.
   d. prevented DNA from transforming into protein molecules.

_____   **6.** Avery and his research team concluded that
   a. RNA was the genetic material.
   b. protein bases were the genetic material.
   c. DNA and RNA were found in the human nucleus.
   d. DNA was the genetic material.

_____   **7.** The scientists credited with establishing the structure of DNA are
   a. Avery and Chargaff.   **c.** Mendel and Griffith.
   b. Hershey and Chase.   **d.** Watson and Crick.

_____   **8.** A gene may be described as
   a. a sequence of amino acids.
   b. special proteins found in chromosomes.
   c. a sequence of nucleotides that codes for a specific protein.
   d. a sequence of nucleotides that codes for the production of starches and sugars.

_____   **9.** In the life cycle of a cell, DNA replication occurs during the
   a. synthesis phase.   **c.** second growth phase.
   b. resting phase.   **d.** first growth phase.

_____   **10.** The enzyme responsible for unwinding the DNA double helix is called DNA
   a. polymerase.   **c.** anhydrase.
   b. amylase.   **d.** helicase.

_____ 11. The process by which DNA polymerase is able to correct mismatched nucleotides is called

   a. proofreading.
   b. replication.
   c. transformation.
   d. substitution.

_____ 12. The combined efforts of approximately 100 replication forks make it possible to replicate an entire human chromosome in about

   a. 18 hours.
   b. 8 days.
   c. 8 minutes.
   d. 8 hours.

Questions 13–15 refer to the figure below.

Phosphate group P

Nitrogen base

Sugar

_____ 13. The molecule shown above is called a(n)

   a. amino acid.
   b. nucleotide.
   c. polysaccharide.
   d. pyrimidine.

_____ 14. In DNA, four forms of this molecule each have a different type of

   a. phosphate group.
   b. sugar.
   c. nitrogen base.
   d. None of the above

_____ 15. The part of the molecule for which deoxyribonucleic acid is named is the

   a. phosphate group.
   b. sugar.
   c. nitrogen base.
   d. None of the above

Complete each statement by writing the correct term or phrase in the space provided.

16. In Griffith's experiments, *R* bacteria were mixed with heat-killed *S* bacteria, and as a result, the harmless *R* bacteria became virulent *S* bacteria. This changing

of the pheonotype of the organisms is called _____ .

17. The process by which DNA copies itself is called DNA _____ .

18. During DNA replication, the enzyme _____

_____ adds complementary nucleotides to each DNA strand, forming two new double helixes.

19. Wilkins and Franklin developed photographs of the DNA molecule using a

method called X-ray _____.

20. Watson and Crick determined that DNA molecules have the shape of a(n)

_____ _____ .

Read each question, and write your answer in the space provided.

21. Summarize the experiments performed by Hershey and Chase that indicated that DNA was probably the genetic material.

_____

_____

_____

_____

22. Identify the major discoveries that led to Watson and Crick's development of the double helix model for DNA.

_____

_____

_____

_____

23. Describe how a molecule of DNA is replicated.

_____

_____

_____

_____

24. Explain how during DNA replication errors in the nucleotide sequence are corrected.

_____

_____

25. Compare the replication process in bacterial DNA with that in human DNA.

_____

_____

_____

Name _____ _____ Date _____ Class _____

How Proteins Are Made

Circle T *if the statement is true or* F *if it is false.*

T   F   **1.** During transcription, the information on a DNA molecule is "rewritten" into an mRNA molecule.

T   F   **2.** A functional ribosome forms when mRNA, two rRNA subunits, and a molecule of tRNA bind together.

T   F   **3.** The operator portion of an operon controls RNA polymerase's access to a group of genes involved in the same function.

T   F   **4.** Gene regulation in eukaryotic and prokaryotic cells is identical.

T   F   **5.** Mutations may prevent evolution from occurring because they introduce genetic variation into a population.

In the space provided, write the letter of the term or phrase that best completes each statement or best answers each question.

_____   **6.** RNA differs from DNA in that RNA

        a. is single-stranded.   **c.** contains uracil.
        b. contains a different sugar.   **d.** All of the above

_____   **7.** After mRNA has been transcribed in eukaryotes,

        a. its introns are cut out.
        b. its exons are joined together.
        c. it leaves the nucleus through pores.
        d. All of the above

_____   **8.** At the beginning of translation, the first tRNA molecule

        a. binds to the ribosome's A site.
        b. attaches directly to the DNA codon.
        c. connects an amino acid to its anticodon.
        d. attaches to the P site of the ribosome.

_____   **9.** The enzyme that adds and links complementary RNA nucleotides during transcription is called

        a. RNA polymerase.
        b. DNA polymerase.
        c. an operon.
        d. an enhancer.

_____   **10.** An operon is composed of the following:

        a. a group of proteins, their promoter site, and their operator.
        b. a group of genes, their operator, and RNA polymerase.
        c. a group of genes, their promoter site, and their operator.
        d. an enhancer, an operator, and RNA polymerase.

_____   **11.** Regulatory proteins in eukaryotes that are involved in controlling the onset of transcription are called

        a. repressors.   **c.** operators.
        b. transcription factors.   **d.** enhancers.

_____ **12.** A frameshift mutation can result from

　　a. a shift in a nucleotide reading sequence.
　　b. substitution of a nucleotide.
　　c. two nucleotides switching places.
　　d. None of the above

_____ **13.** If a deletion mutation eliminated all of the guanine bases from the codon sequence GAT-CGC-CAA-TAG, the altered sequence would read

　　a. ATC-TCA-ATA. 　　　　　　**c.** ACC-CAA-ATA.
　　b. ATC-CCA-ATA. 　　　　　　**d.** AAT-CCA-TAC.

Questions 14–16 refer to the mRNA sequence CUC-AAG-UGC-UUC and the table below, which lists mRNA codons.

Codons in mRNA					
First base	**Second base**				**Third base**
	U	**C**	**A**	**G**	
U	UUU ⎤ Phenylalanine UUC ⎦ UUA ⎤ Leucine UUG ⎦	UCU ⎤ UCC ⎥ Serine UCA ⎥ UCG ⎦	UAU ⎤ Tyrosine UAC ⎦ UAA ⎤ Stop UAG ⎦	UGU ⎤ Cysteine UGC ⎦ UGA – Stop UGG – Tryptophan	U C A G
C	CUU ⎤ CUC ⎥ Leucine CUA ⎥ CUG ⎦	CCU ⎤ CCC ⎥ Proline CCA ⎥ CCG ⎦	CAU ⎤ Histidine CAC ⎦ CAA ⎤ Glutamine CAG ⎦	CGU ⎤ CGC ⎥ Arginine CGA ⎥ CGG ⎦	U C A G
A	AUU ⎤ AUC ⎥ Isoleucine AUA ⎦ AUG – Start	ACU ⎤ ACC ⎥ Threonine ACA ⎥ ACG ⎦	AAU ⎤ Asparagine AAC ⎦ AAA ⎤ Lysine AAG ⎦	AGU ⎤ Serine AGC ⎦ AGA ⎤ Arginine AGG ⎦	U C A G
G	GUU ⎤ GUC ⎥ Valine GUA ⎥ GUG ⎦	GCU ⎤ GCC ⎥ Alanine GCA ⎥ GCG ⎦	GAU ⎤ Aspartic acid GAC ⎦ GAA ⎤ Glutamic acid GAG ⎦	GGU ⎤ GGC ⎥ Glycine GGA ⎥ GGG ⎦	U C A G

_____ **14.** Which of the following would represent the sequence of DNA from which the mRNA sequence was made?

　　a. CUC-AAG-UGC-UUC 　　　**c.** GAG-TTC-ACG-AAG
　　b. GAG-UUC-ACG-AAG 　　　**d.** AGA-CCT-GTA-GGA

_____ **15.** The anticodons for the codons in the mRNA sequence above are

　　a. GAG-UUC-ACG-AAG. 　　　**c.** CUC-GAA-CGU-CUU.
　　b. GAG-TTC-ACG-AAG. 　　　**d.** CUU-CGU-GAA-CUC.

_____ **16.** Use the table to determine which of the following represents the portion of the protein molecule coded for by the mRNA sequence above.

　　a. serine - tyrosine - arginine - glycine
　　b. valine - aspartic acid - proline - histidine
　　c. leucine - lysine - cysteine - phenylalanine
　　d. glutamic acid - phenylalanine - threonine - lysine

Complete each statement by writing the correct term or phrase in the space provided.

17. The information contained in a molecule of mRNA is used to make

    protein during the process of _____ .

18. Nucleotide sequences of tRNA that are complementary to codons on mRNA

    are called _____ .

19. _____ are regions of DNA that stimulate transcription of certain genes.

20. Comparing the nucleotide sequence of genes that have an unknown sequence with the sequence in corresponding healthy genes is one way of detecting a(n)

    _____ _____ .

Read each question, and write your answer in the space provided.

21. Distinguish between transcription and translation.

    _____

    _____

    _____

22. Explain the evolutionary significance of the fact that the base sequence GUC codes for the amino acid valine in so many different species.

    _____

    _____

23. How is RNA polymerase affected by the presence of lactose in bacterial cells?

    _____

    _____

    _____

24. Briefly describe introns.

    _____

    _____

25. What is a point mutation? Name two kinds of point mutations.

    _____

    _____

    _____

Name_____ Date _____ Class_____

Gene Technology

Circle T *if the statement is true or* F *if it is false.*

T   F   **1.** Researchers are now able to clone animals using differentiated cells.

T   F   **2.** Technological advances have now made it possible to transfer healthy copies of a gene into the cells of a person whose copy of the gene is defective.

T   F   **3.** The genomes of more than 15 organisms have already been completely sequenced.

T   F   **4.** Genetic engineers have developed a method for adding human genes to the genes of farm animals in order to get the farm animals to produce human proteins in their milk. The human proteins are then extracted from the animals' milk and sold for pharmaceutical purposes.

In the space provided, write the letter of the term or phrase that best completes each statement or best answers each question.

_____ **5.** Recombinant DNA is formed by joining DNA molecules
   a. from two different species.
   b. with a carbohydrate from a different species.
   c. with RNA molecules.
   d. with a protein from a different species.

_____ **6.** Plasmids
   a. are circular pieces of bacterial DNA.
   b. can replicate independently of the organism's main chromosome.
   c. are often used as vectors in genetic engineering experiments.
   d. All of the above

_____ **7.** Fragments of DNA that have complementary "sticky ends"
   a. are found only in bacterial cells.
   b. can join with each other.
   c. can only join with complementary fragments from the same species.
   d. are immediately digested by enzymes in the cytoplasm of the cell.

_____ **8.** Genetic engineering experiments use tetracycline to
   a. prevent the cell cultures from becoming infected.
   b. kill the cells that had the recombinant DNA.
   c. identify cells that have taken up the recombined vector DNA.
   d. None of the above

_____ **9.** The risk associated with vaccines prepared from dead or weakened pathogenic microbes is that
   a. a few remaining live or unweakened microbes could still cause the disease.
   b. the antibodies that result may not work.
   c. the vaccine protects only against other diseases.
   d. None of the above

_____ 10. A cell that has specialized and become a specific type of cell is called a
   a. clone.
   b. plasmid.
   c. transgenic cell.
   d. differentiated cell.

_____ 11. A gene that codes for resistance to glyphosate has been added to the genome of certain plants. These plants will
   a. produce chemicals that kill weeds growing near them.
   b. die when exposed to glyphosate.
   c. convert glyphosate into fertilizer.
   d. survive when glyphosate is applied to the field.

_____ 12. Genetic engineers are developing approaches for improving agriculture in all of the following ways EXCEPT
   a. making plants resistant to insects.
   b. making certain plants susceptible to Ti plasmids.
   c. making plants more tolerant of drought conditions.
   d. improving the nutritional value of certain plants.

_____ 13. Upon its expected completion in the year 2003, the Human Genome Project will have
   a. successfully identified the sequences and locations of all human genes.
   b. significantly improved the ability to diagnose, treat, and cure human genetic disorders.
   c. accomplished a major effort in gene technology.
   d. All of the above

Complete each statement by writing the correct term or phrase in the space provided.

14. The process used to isolate a gene from the DNA of one organism and transfer that gene into the DNA of another organism (for practical purposes) is called

   _____ _____ .

15. The pattern of dark bands on X-ray film made when an individual's DNA fragments are separated, probed, and then exposed to an X-ray film is

   called a(n) _____ _____ .

16. Small, circular forms of bacterial DNA that can replicate independently of the

   main bacterial chromosome are called _____ .

17. Genetically identical cells grown from a single cell are called

   _____ .

18. Enzymes that cut DNA at specific sequences, producing fragments of DNA,

   are called _____ _____ .

19. Scientists use a technique called a(n) _____

_____ to confirm that the cloned gene of interest is present in a bacterial colony.

20. Radioactive or fluorescent-labeled RNA or single-stranded DNA pieces that are complementary to the gene of interest are called _____ .

21. A(n) _____ is a solution that contains a dead or modified version of a pathogen or its toxins.

Read each question, and write your answer in the space provided.

22. Summarize the four steps of a genetic engineering experiment.

_____

_____

_____

_____

_____

_____

_____

23. Describe two different uses for DNA fingerprints.

_____

_____

_____

24. Explain how scientists use tumor necrosis factor (TNF) to fight cancer.

_____

_____

_____

25. Explain how gel electrophoresis is used in genetic engineering experiments.

_____

_____

_____

Name_____ Date _____ Class _____

History of Life on Earth

Circle T *if the statement is true or* F *if it is false.*

T F **1.** Oxygen was found in the atmosphere millions of years before it was present in the oceans.

T F **2.** The first multicellular creatures to populate the land were animals that came from the ocean.

T F **3.** Both the primordial soup and bubble models require ammonia, methane, and other hydrogen-containing gases to make amino acids.

T F **4.** Amphibians can lay their eggs on dry land because the eggs are surrounded by a shell that prevents water loss.

T F **5.** The theory of endosymbiosis states that bacteria invaded pre-eukaryotic cells and gave rise to mitochondria and chloroplasts.

In the space provided, write the letter of the term or phrase that best completes each statement or best answers each question.

_____ **6.** Cyanobacteria changed early Earth's atmosphere by giving off
  a. carbon dioxide.
  b. ammonia.
  c. hydrogen.
  d. oxygen.

_____ **7.** All the living things on Earth today are grouped into
  a. three kingdoms.
  b. four kingdoms.
  c. five kingdoms.
  d. six kingdoms.

_____ **8.** Eukaryotes may have descended from
  a. eubacteria.
  b. archaebacteria.
  c. cyanobacteria.
  d. None of the above

_____ **9.** Determining the age of a rock by comparing relative proportions of its radioactive isotopes is called
  a. radioactive dating.
  b. radiometric dating.
  c. radioisotope dating.
  d. All of the above

_____ **10.** Protists were the first organisms to exhibit cell specialization, which was only possible when they
  a. grew large enough.
  b. became eukaryotic.
  c. evolved into fungi, plants, and animals.
  d. became multicellular.

_____ **11.** The first step toward cellular organization may have been the gathering of amino acids into
   a. macromolecules.
   b. coacervates.
   c. microspheres.
   d. DNA molecules.

_____ **12.** Organisms were able to live safely on dry land after
   a. cyanobacteria made oxygen and ozone began to form.
   b. the fifth mass extinction.
   c. continental drift stopped.
   d. archaebacteria made oxygen and ozone began to form.

_____ **13.** Which of the following enabled the beginning of life as we know it?
   a. the ozone layer
   b. heredity
   c. microspheres
   d. endosymbiosis

_____ **14.** The first animals to live successfully on land were
   a. amphibians.
   b. reptiles.
   c. arthropods.
   d. flying insects.

_____ **15.** In mycorrhizae, fungi provide
   a. food to plants.
   b. energy to plants.
   c. minerals to plants.
   d. All of the above

_____ **16.** Prokaryotes that lack peptidoglycan in their cell walls are called
   a. eubacteria.
   b. *Escherichia coli.*
   c. pre-eukaryotes.
   d. archaebacteria.

Complete each statement by writing the correct term or phrase in the space provided.

17. _____ were the first eukaryotes.

18. At the end of the _____ period 250 million years ago, about 96 percent of all species of animals became extinct.

19. Ozone forms a protective layer in the atmosphere and absorbs

_____ radiation.

20. _____ were the first vertebrates to live on land.

21. The most successful living vertebrates are _____ .

22. Three successful kingdoms that evolved from protists are

_____ , _____ , and

_____ .

23. _____ , the most numerous group of animals on Earth,

probably owe their success to the evolution of _____ .

Read each question, and write your answer in the space provided.

24. Briefly summarize the five steps of Louis Lerman's model of spontaneous origin.

_____

_____

_____

_____

_____

_____

25. Why has there been a burst of evolution after each of the great mass extinctions?

_____

_____

_____

_____

_____

_____

_____

CHAPTER

13 **TEST**

The Theory of Evolution

Circle T *if the statement is true or* F *if it is false.*

T F **1.** Animals located close together on a phylogenetic tree have fewer nucleotide differences than those located farther apart.

T F **2.** The way an embryo develops is not important in determining the evolutionary history of a species.

T F **3.** *Gradualism* refers to the hypothesis that evolution occurs slowly over a long period of time.

T F **4.** Within a population, divergence leads to speciation.

In the space provided, write the letter of the term or phrase that best completes each statement or best answers each question.

_____ **5.** The evolution of beak sizes in Galápagos finches is a response to
   a. how finches use their beaks.
   b. the types of seeds available.
   c. whether the populations interbreed.
   d. the nutritional content of the seeds.

_____ **6.** According to Darwin, evolution occurs
   a. by chance.
   b. over a half-life of 5,730 years.
   c. by natural selection.
   d. rapidly.

_____ **7.** The hypothesis that evolution occurs at a rapid rate, separated by periods of no change,
   a. was supported by Darwin.
   b. is known as punctuated equilibrium.
   c. is supported by many transitional forms in the fossil record.
   d. was proposed by Lyell.

_____ **8.** The traits of individuals best adapted to survive become more common in each new generation because
   a. offspring without those traits do not survive.
   b. the alleles responsible for those traits increase through natural selection.
   c. those individuals interbreed.
   d. natural selection does not affect well-adapted individuals.

_____ **9.** Natural selection causes
   a. changes in the environment.
   b. plants and animals to produce more offspring than can survive.
   c. changes in the frequency of certain alleles in a population.
   d. All of the above

_____ **10.** In his experiments with peppered moths, Kettlewell found that
  a. the color of the moths was not important.
  b. birds preferred the flavor of light-colored moths.
  c. moths that matched the color of the tree trunks were
     more likely to survive.
  d. coloration was an inherited trait.

_____ **11.** That organisms produce more offspring than their environment can
     support and that they compete with one another to survive are
  a. elements of natural selection.   **c.** the only mechanisms of evolution.
  b. not elements of evolution.   **d.** the beginning of speciation.

_____ **12.** Natural selection is the process by which
  a. the age of Earth is calculated.
  b. organisms with traits well suited to the environment survive and
     reproduce at a greater rate than other organisms.
  c. acquired traits are passed from one generation to the next.
  d. All of the above

_____ **13.** The theory of evolution predicts that
  a. closely related species will show similarities in nucleotide sequences.
  b. if species have changed over time, their genes should have changed.
  c. closely related species will show similarities in amino acid sequences.
  d. All of the above

Questions 14–16 refer to the figures below.

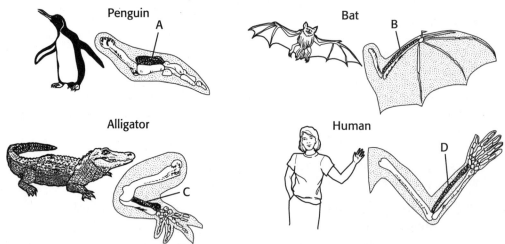

_____ **14.** The bones labeled *A–D* are known as
  a. vestigial structures.   **c.** homologous structures.
  b. sequential structures.   **d.** fossil structures.

_____ **15.** The similarity of these structures suggests that the organisms
  a. have a common ancestor.   **c.** evolved slowly.
  b. all grow at different rates.   **d.** live for a long time.

_____ **16.** An analysis of the DNA from these organisms would indicate that
  a. their DNA is identical.
  b. they all have gill pouches.
  c. their nucleotide sequences show many similarities.
  d. they all have the same number of chromosomes.

Complete each statement by writing the correct term or phrase in the space provided.

17. The _____ determines the direction and amount of change in a species.

18. Structures that are present in an organism but are reduced in size and have

    little or no function are called _____ structures.

19. Homologous structures are similar between species because they are inherited

    from a common _____ .

20. Organisms produce more offspring than can _____ .

21. The most direct evidence for evolution comes from _____ ,

    which provide records of past life-forms through _____ ,

    _____ remains, or imprints of organisms.

22. Darwin's theory of evolution states that _____

    _____ is the mechanism of evolution.

23. When Darwin observed the similarities between plants and animals of the Galápagos Islands and South America, he proposed that ancestors of the

    Galápagos species migrated and underwent _____ with

    _____ .

Read each question, and write your answer in the space provided.

24. An agricultural plot of land is sprayed with a very powerful insecticide to destroy harmful insects. Nevertheless, many of the same species of insects are present on the land the following year. How might Darwin's theory account for this phenomenon?

    _____

    _____

    _____

25. What role does the environment play in natural selection?

    _____

    _____

    _____

Human Evolution

Circle T *if the statement is true or* F *if it is false.*

T F **1.** Primate ancestors had unbendable toes and binocular vision.

T F **2.** Fossil evidence indicates that most extinct primate species lived in trees.

T F **3.** Apes and humans are classified as hominids.

T F **4.** Scientists think that early *Homo sapiens* had language capability.

T F **5.** The hominid that arose most recently is *Homo sapiens.*

In the space provided, write the letter of the term or phrase that best completes each statement or best answers each question.

_____ **6.** Monkeys
    a. are day-active prosimians.
    b. have larger brains than prosimians.
    c. have binocular vision.
    d. All of the above

_____ **7.** Dart's fossil discovery in 1924 was the first evidence of a prehuman that
    a. walked upright.
    b. had a larger brain volume than apes.
    c. did not have an ape's pointed jaw.
    d. All of the above

_____ **8.** Because DNA sequences in humans and chimpanzees are very similar,
    a. humans must have evolved from chimpanzees.
    b. chimpanzees must have single-stranded DNA.
    c. humans and chimpanzees must have a common ancestor in very recent geologic history.
    d. humans and chimpanzees are the same species.

_____ **9.** Most scientists agree that the oldest known hominid belonged to the genus
    a. *Homo.*
    b. *Australopithecus.*
    c. *Ardipithecus.*
    d. *Neanderthecus.*

_____ **10.** An examination of australopithecine fossils indicates that australopithecines
    a. were taller than modern humans.
    b. were bipedal.
    c. had arms that were longer than their legs.
    d. All of the above

_____ **11.** The name *Homo habilis* translates roughly as
    a. "hairy ape."   **c.** "handy man."
    b. "human habitat."   **d.** "apelike human."

_____ **12.** *Homo erectus*

    a. lived in Africa, Asia, and Europe.

    b. walked upright.

    c. was larger than *Homo habilis*.

    d. All of the above

_____ **13.** Which statement about monkeys and apes is NOT true?

    a. Both have opposable thumbs.

    b. Apes have relatively larger brains.

    c. Both have color vision.

    d. Both have tails.

Questions 14–16 refer to the figures below, which show the skeletons of two primates.

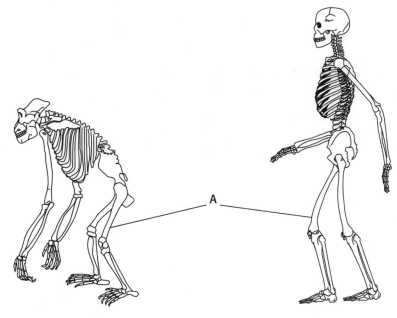

Skeleton 1   **Skeleton 2**

_____ **14.** The bone labeled *A* is the

    a. pelvis.   **c.** humerus.

    b. femur.   **d.** spine.

_____ **15.** Skeleton 2 is probably the skeleton of a

    a. chimpanzee.   **c.** bonobo.

    b. gorilla.   **d.** hominid.

_____ **16.** By examining the skeletons, scientists conclude that organism 1

    a. could walk upright, but not too efficiently.

    b. has a spine that makes walking upright very easy.

    c. has arms and legs that are both used for walking.

    d. Both (a) and (c)

Complete each statement by writing the correct term or phrase in the space provided.

17. Primates have _____ hands and feet that allow them to grip limbs.

18. The position of the eyes in primates allows them to have

    _____ vision.

19. The first primates were members of the mostly night-active group called

    _____ .

20. Analysis of _____ DNA indicates that *Homo sapiens* evolved in Africa.

21. *Homo habilis* were more evolutionarily advanced than australopithecines

    because *Homo habilis* had larger _____ and used

    _____ .

22. The direct ancestor of both modern humans and Neanderthals is

    _____ _____ .

Read each question, and write your answer in the space provided.

23. Summarize the two hypotheses about how and where *Homo sapiens* evolved.

    _____

    _____

    _____

    _____

24. What information is known about Tim White's fossil discovery in 1992?

    _____

    _____

    _____

25. Why was the evolution of a large brain important in primate evolution?

    _____

    _____

    _____

    _____

CHAPTER
15 **TEST**

Classification of Organisms

Circle T *if the statement is true or* F *if it is false.*

T   F   **1.** Aristotle developed the first system of binomial nomenclature.

T   F   **2.** Biologists use cladograms to evaluate the importance of characteristics.

T   F   **3.** Linnaeus's two-word system for naming organisms is called binomial nomenclature.

T   F   **4.** Linnaeus's naming system, developed in the 1750s, relied on the concept of biological species.

T   F   **5.** Related genera are grouped into the same family.

In the space provided, write the letter of the term or phrase that best completes each statement or best answers each question.

_____ **6.** The science of naming and classifying organisms is called
    a. binomial nomenclature.   **c.** taxonomy.
    b. polynomial nomenclature.   **d.** evolutionary systematics.

_____ **7.** Linnaeus developed a new naming system because
    a. he disagreed with the current classifications.
    b. the polynomial system was too complicated.
    c. the old one did not use Latin.
    d. the polynomial system's descriptions were too brief.

_____ **8.** Which of the following do biologists NOT use to classify organisms?
    a. homologous structures   **c.** appearance
    b. derived traits   **d.** analogous structures

_____ **9.** An organism's scientific name consists of its
    a. genus and species.
    b. genus and family.
    c. species and family.
    d. common name and Latin name.

_____ **10.** Biological species, as defined by Ernst Mayr, are
    a. always closely related.
    b. always reproductively isolated.
    c. members of different genera.
    d. None of the above

_____ **11.** Honeybees, as members of the kingdom Animalia, are related to
    a. wasps.   **c.** spiders.
    b. birds.   **d.** All of the above

_____ **12.** Linnaeus's classification system was based on which of the following characteristics?
    a. form and structure   **c.** behavior
    b. DNA   **d.** phylogenetic relationships

Questions 13 and 14 refer to the table below.

Classification of Three Different Organisms				
Organism	**Class**	**A**	**Family**	**Genus**
Bacterium	Scotobacteria	Spirochaetales	Spirochaetaceae	*Cristispira*
Box elder	Dicotyledones	Sapindales	Aceraceae	*Acer*
Human	Mammalia	Primates	Hominidae	**B**

_____ 13. Which level of classification is represented by the box labeled *A*?

   a. kingdom   **c.** division
   b. phylum   **d.** order

_____ 14. Which of the following best fits the box labeled *B*?

   a. *sapiens*   **c.** *Homo*
   b. *Canis*   **d.** Animalia

Complete each statement by writing the correct term or phrase in the space provided.

15. The method of evaluating evolutionary relationships in a group of organisms when a great deal of information is known about the organisms is

   called _____ _____ .

16. If a Latin term describing an organism is underlined or italicized, the term is

   either the _____ or the _____ name.

17. The interbreeding of wolves and dogs to produce fertile offspring is an

   example of incomplete _____ barriers.

18. The seven major classification groups, starting with species and ending with

   kingdom, go from _____ inclusive to _____ inclusive.

19. The _____ of a species is its evolutionary history.

20. In the scientific name for the sandhill crane, *G. canadensis*, *canadensis* is the

   _____ , and *G.* is an abbreviation of the _____ .

21. The biological species concept fails to describe species that reproduce

   _____ .

22. _____ is a system of taxonomy in which biologists infer relationships based on similiarities to classify organisms.

Name _____ Date _____ Class _____

Read each question, and write your answer in the space provided.

23. Under what circumstances might a scientist choose cladistics over evolutionary systematics to classify an organism or a group of organisms?

_____

_____

_____

_____

_____

24. Are the levels of biological classification more closely associated with cladistics or evolutionary systematics? Explain.

_____

_____

_____

_____

_____

25. Assume there is an East Coast duck species and a West Coast duck species whose ranges meet in the middle of the United States. The males of one species are blue, and the males of the other species are green. The females of both species look alike. Their diets are similar and they build nests at the water's edge. Why is it likely that these two species will produce hybrids?

_____

_____

_____

_____

_____

CHAPTER
(16) **TEST**

Populations

Circle T *if the statement is true or* F *if it is false.*

T F **1.** Very small populations are less likely to become extinct than larger populations.

T F **2.** If individuals are evenly dispersed, their locations are self-determined.

T F **3.** The logistic population growth model considers the declining availability of resources.

T F **4.** Populations of *K*-strategists grow rapidly, while *r*-strategist populations grow slowly.

T F **5.** Gene flow is the movement of alleles into or out of a population, while genetic drift is the random change in allele frequency.

T F **6.** Natural selection always eliminates any genetic disorders from a population, regardless of the frequency of the genes that are responsible for the disorders.

In the space provided, write the letter of the term or phrase that best completes each statement or best answers each question.

_____ **7.** Which of the following does NOT represent a population?
  a. all the robins in Austin, Texas
  b. all the grass frogs in a pond in Central Park, New York City
  c. all the birds in Chicago, Illinois
  d. all the black bears in Yosemite National Park

_____ **8.** Actual proportions of homozygotes and heterozygotes can differ from Hardy-Weinberg predictions because of
  a. the occurrence of mutations.
  b. nonrandom mating among individuals.
  c. genetic drift within the population.
  d. All of the above

_____ **9.** The movement of alleles into or out of a population is called
  a. mutation.   **c.** nonrandom mating.
  b. gene flow.   **d.** natural selection.

_____ **10.** Inbreeding
  a. is a form of random mating.
  b. causes mutations to occur.
  c. increases the proportion of heterozygotes.
  d. increases the proportion of homozygotes.

_____ **11.** Allele frequency is affected least by
  a. genetic drift.   **c.** mutations.
  b. gene flow.   **d.** Both (b) and (c)

_____ **12.** Natural selection shapes populations by acting on

    a. genes.
    b. recessive alleles.
    c. phenotypes.
    d. All of the above

_____ **13.** The type of selection that may eliminate extremes of phenotypes is called

    a. directional selection.
    b. disruptive selection.
    c. polygenic selection.
    d. stabilizing selection.

_____ **14.** Directional selection is characteristic of

    a. populations living in environments that do not change much.
    b. the evolution of single-gene traits.
    c. intermediate phenotypes.
    d. None of the above

Questions 15–18 refer to the figure below, which shows population growth over time.

Population Growth

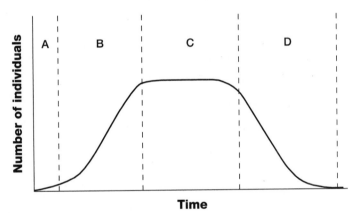

_____ **15.** Which time period shows exponential growth of the population?

    a. *A*
    b. *B*
    c. *C*
    d. *D*

_____ **16.** During which time period are the birth rate and death rate equal?

    a. *A*
    b. *B*
    c. *C*
    d. *D*

_____ **17.** The rate of growth of a population is represented by *r*. During which time period will *r* equal zero?

    a. *A*
    b. *B*
    c. *C*
    d. *D*

_____ **18.** The time period during which *r* would have a negative value is labeled

    a. *A.*
    b. *B.*
    c. *C.*
    d. *D.*

Name _____ Date _____ Class _____

Complete each statement by writing the correct term or phrase in the space provided.

19. The _____ _____ is the population size that can be sustained by an environment.

20. Species that are _____ tend to have periods of exponential growth followed by sudden decreases in population size.

21. Small population sizes and slow population growth are typical of species

    that are _____ .

22. _____ selection causes the range of phenotypes to become narrower, increasing the number of individuals with characteristics near the middle of the range.

23. _____ _____ , as a result of genetic drift, can decrease a population's resistance to disease.

24. The Hardy-Weinberg principle does not apply when _____

    _____ act upon populations.

Read each question, and write your answer in the space provided.

25. Explain how natural selection changes populations.

    _____

    _____

    _____

    _____

    _____

Ecosystems

Circle T *if the statement is true or* F *if it is false.*

T　F　**1.** An ecosystem consists of all the living organisms and their biotic factors.

T　F　**2.** Producers are at the bottom of ecological pyramids.

T　F　**3.** During nitrification, decomposers break down the roots of plants to produce nitrates.

T　F　**4.** Consumers get energy from the sun or by eating producers.

T　F　**5.** Grizzly bears, snakes, and worms can be members of the same ecosystem.

In the space provided, write the letter of the term or phrase that best completes each statement or best answers each question.

_____ **6.** All the organisms that live in a particular place and the physical aspects of that place make up a(n)
　　a. ecosystem.
　　b. habitat.
　　c. community.
　　d. food chain.

_____ **7.** The number of species living in an ecosystem is referred to as
　　a. succession.
　　b. biodiversity.
　　c. the food chain.
　　d. productivity.

_____ **8.** The most important abiotic factor for the organisms in an ecosystem is
　　a. climate.
　　b. sun.
　　c. weather.
　　d. water.

_____ **9.** Animals that feed on plants are at least in the
　　a. first trophic level.
　　b. second trophic level.
　　c. third trophic level.
　　d. fourth trophic level.

_____ **10.** The number of trophic levels in an ecological pyramid
　　a. is limitless.
　　b. is limited by the amount of energy that is lost at each trophic level.
　　c. never exceeds four.
　　d. never exceeds three.

_____ **11.** The movement of substances, such as water and nitrogen, in a circular path between the nonliving environment and living organisms is called
　　a. a reservoir pathway.
　　b. photosynthesis.
　　c. a biogeochemical cycle.
　　d. succession.

_____ **12.** In a typical primary succession initiated by a retreating glacier,
　　a. lichens and mosses precede trees.
　　b. the first plants are stunted by mineral deficiencies.
　　c. it takes about 10 years for trees to be able to thrive.
　　d. All of the above

Name_____ Date _____ Class _____

Questions 13–15 refer to the figure below, which shows the feeding relationships in an Antarctic ecosystem.

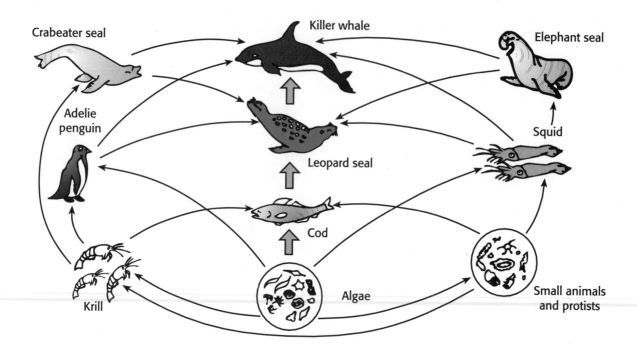

_____ **13.** The figure above represents a
  a. trophic net.
  b. food chain.
  c. food net.
  d. food web.

_____ **14.** The algae are
  a. producers.
  b. consumers.
  c. parasites.
  d. decomposers.

_____ **15.** Leopard seals are
  a. producers.
  b. omnivores.
  c. herbivores.
  d. carnivores.

Complete each statement by writing the correct term or phrase in the space provided.

16. The organisms in a trophic level can store only about _____

_____ as much energy as the organisms in the next lowest level.

17. Organisms that obtain their energy from the organic wastes and dead bodies

at all the energy levels in an ecosystem are called _____ .

18. Examples of elements that are recycled in an ecosystem include carbon,

nitrogen, _____ , _____ , and

_____ .

19. Every time energy is transferred in an ecosystem, potential energy is lost as

_____ .

20. The path of _____ through trophic levels is called a food chain.

A network of intertwined food chains is called a(n) _____

_____ .

21. Plants return water to the atmosphere through _____ .

22. The conversion of atmospheric _____ _____
to ammonia by bacteria in the soil or on plant roots is called

_____ _____ .

Read each question, and write your answer in the space provided.

23. Why is it cheaper for a farmer to produce a pound of grain than a pound
of meat?

_____

_____

_____

_____

24. Why are decomposers necessary for the continuation of life on Earth?

_____

_____

_____

_____

25. Explain the importance of the carbon cycle to living organisms.

_____

_____

_____

_____

CHAPTER
18 **TEST**

Biological Communities

Circle T *if the statement is true or* F *if it is false.*

T   F   **1.** A long-term relationship in which both participating species benefit is known as parasitism.

T   F   **2.** Thorns, spines, and secondary compounds are examples of coevolution.

T   F   **3.** Permafrost is a characteristic of the taiga.

T   F   **4.** When two species compete for limited resources, competitive exclusion is sure to take place.

T   F   **5.** About 2 percent of Earth's surface is fresh water, and 75 percent is ocean.

In the space provided, write the letter of the term or phrase that best completes each statement or best answers each question.

_____   **6.** The evolution of flowers and the insects that feed on them is known as
      a. parasitism.   **c.** coevolution.
      b. secondary succession.   **d.** stability.

_____   **7.** A tick feeding on a human is an example of
      a. parasitism.   **c.** symbiosis.
      b. mutualism.   **d.** predation.

_____   **8.** An organism's niche includes
      a. what it eats.   **c.** how it reproduces.
      b. where it eats.   **d.** All of the above

_____   **9.** Over time, pressure from predators will cause prey species to evolve
      a. parasitism.   **c.** secondary compounds.
      b. into a new niche.   **d.** ways to avoid predation.

_____   **10.** Tropical rain forests are found close to the equator because
      a. rainfall is highest at lower latitudes.
      b. soil is most fertile at lower latitudes.
      c. rainfall varies from season to season near the equator.
      d. rainfall averages 80 cm per year at the equator.

_____   **11.** Which of the following determines what organisms can live in a particular biological community?
      a. climate   **c.** temperature
      b. rainfall   **d.** all of the above

_____   **12.** Compared with a forest that contains 25 different plant species, a forest that contains 55 different plant species is
      a. larger and more stable.
      b. more productive and more stable.
      c. older and more productive.
      d. older and larger.

_____ **13.** An ecologist studying an ocean ecosystem performed an experiment in which predatory sea stars were removed from the ecosystem. After the removal of the sea stars,

    a. the ecosystem became more diverse.

    b. the size of the ecosystem was reduced.

    c. food webs in the ecosystem became more complex.

    d. the number of species in the ecosystem was reduced.

Questions 14–17 refer to the figures below, which illustrate experiments performed with two species of barnacles that live in the same area.

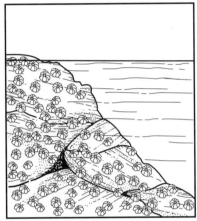
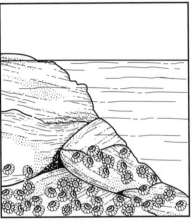
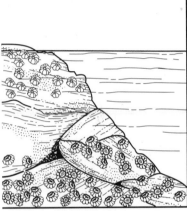

A. The barnacle *Chthamalus stellatus* can live in both shallow and deep water on a rocky coast.

B. The barnacle *Balanus balanoides* lives mostly in deep water.

C. When the two barnacles live together, *Chthamalus* is restricted to shallow water.

_____ **14.** Figure A indicates that *Chthamalus stellatus* can live in both shallow and deep water on a rocky coast. This is the barnacle's

    a. competitive niche.   **c.** fundamental niche.

    b. realized niche.   **d.** exclusive niche.

_____ **15.** Figure B indicates that *Balanus balanoides* lives mostly in deep water. Deep water is this barnacle's

    a. competitive niche.   **c.** fundamental niche.

    b. realized niche.   **d.** exclusive niche.

_____ **16.** Figure C indicates that when the two barnacles live together, *Chthamalus* is restricted to shallow water. Shallow water is its

    a. competitive niche.   **c.** fundamental niche.

    b. realized niche.   **d.** exclusive niche.

_____ **17.** Because the two species of barnacles attempt to use the same resources, they are

    a. parasitic.

    b. in competition with one another.

    c. mutualistic.

    d. symbiotic.

Name_____ Date _____ Class _____

Complete each statement by writing the correct term or phrase in the space provided.

18. The biome with the greatest amount of annual precipitation is the

_____ _____ _____ .

19. A relationship in which one species benefits and the other is neither harmed

nor helped is known as _____ .

20. _____ _____ reduce competition and allow more species to live in a community.

21. Local elimination of one competing species is known as _____

_____ .

22. Coniferous trees are predominantly found in the _____ biome.

23. In freshwater communities, aquatic plants are found in the _____

_____ .

Read each question, and write your answer in the space provided.

24. Can two species occupy the same realized niche? Explain.

_____

_____

_____

_____

_____

_____

25. How are freshwater habitats connected to terrestrial habitats?

_____

_____

_____

_____

_____

_____

Name _____ Date _____ Class _____

Human Impact on the Environment

Circle T *if the statement is true or* F *if it is false.*

T   F   1. Ozone depletion in the upper atmosphere can lead to increased incidence of skin cancer and cataracts.

T   F   2. CFCs are banned as refrigerator coolants but are still allowed as aerosol propellants.

T   F   3. During the last 50 years, about one-half of Earth's tropical rain forests have been destroyed.

T   F   4. One approach to reducing pollution is not to tax the sale of products that cause pollution.

T   F   5. Secondary sewage treatment plants remove chemicals and bacteria from sewage.

In the space provided, write the letter of the term or phrase that best completes each statement or best answers each question.

_____ 6. The loss of species from some lakes in the northeastern United States may best be explained by
  a. global warming.   **c.** the destruction of the ozone layer.
  b. evolutionary trends.   **d.** acid rain.

_____ 7. The heat-trapping ability of some gases in the atmosphere is responsible for
  a. acid rain.
  b. the greenhouse effect.
  c. the breakdown of CFCs.
  d. increased levels of ultraviolet radiation.

_____ 8. Topsoil and ground water
  a. exist in unlimited quantities in aquifers throughout the world.
  b. are found only on the prairie.
  c. are renewable resources.
  d. are nonreplaceable resources.

_____ 9. The human population increases in size when the
  a. death rate equals the birth rate.
  b. death rate exceeds the birth rate.
  c. birth rate equals the death rate.
  d. birth rate exceeds the death rate.

_____ 10. The increase in world population from 5 million people 10,000 years ago to 130 million people 8,000 years later was probably a result of
  a. a drastic reduction in the death rate at the time.
  b. more dependable food sources.
  c. trade routes between the continents.
  d. None of the above

_____ **11.** Risk analysis involves

    a. supplying a population with information.

    b. predicting the consequences of environmental intervention.

    c. political action.

    d. education.

_____ **12.** Human population growth is most rapid in

    a. Europe.   **c.** Japan.

    b. the United States.   **d.** developing countries.

_____ **13.** Molecules of chemical pollutants become increasingly concentrated in higher trophic levels in a process called

    a. biological accumulations.   **c.** biological magnification.

    b. toxic magnification.   **d.** pollutant magnification.

Questions 14 and 15 refer to the figure below.

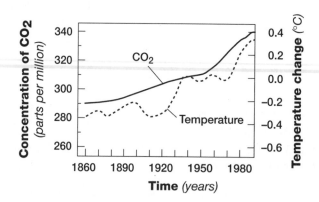

_____ **14.** The graph above shows

    a. the concentration of carbon dioxide in the atmosphere since 1860.

    b. the average global temperature since 1860.

    c. that the concentration of oxygen in the atmosphere has increased since 1860.

    d. None of the above

_____ **15.** According to the graph above,

    a. from 1900 to 1950 the average global temperature constantly increased.

    b. the concentration of carbon dioxide in the atmosphere has increased at the same steady rate for the past 100 years.

    c. the concentration of carbon dioxide and the temperature were the same in 1940.

    d. the temperature has increased since 1980.

Complete each statement by writing the correct term or phrase in the space provided.

16. Ozone in the atmosphere blocks harmful _____ radiation from reaching the surface of Earth.

17. Worldwide, loss of _____ is the most common cause of species extinction.

18. If current projections of world population growth are accurate, Earth may

    not be able to _____ that many people.

19. Earth's human population has increased over the past 350 years because of a

    decrease in the _____ rate of humans.

20. Individuals can do their part in reducing _____ through the
    choices they make in day-to-day activities.

Read each question, and write your answer in the space provided.

21. Explain the effects of biological magnification, using DDT as an example.

    _____

    _____

    _____

    _____

    _____

22. What five steps are followed to solve environmental problems successfully?

    _____

    _____

    _____

    _____

    _____

23. Explain why acid rain was not an environmental issue 200 years ago.

    _____

    _____

24. Why is it important to prevent the extinction of species?

    _____

    _____

25. Describe how chemical pollutants that washed into the Rhine River in
    Switzerland were responsible for killing fish in the North Sea.

    _____

    _____

CHAPTER
20 **TEST**

Introduction to the Kingdoms of Life

Circle T *if the statement is true or* F *if it is false.*

T F **1.** All kingdoms have organisms that are both unicellular and multicellular.

T F **2.** Many archaebacteria are considered primary producers because they obtain much of their energy from organic sources.

T F **3.** Eubacteria are grouped mostly by their shape, the nature of their cell wall, and their type of metabolism.

T F **4.** During times of stress, slime molds form aggregations to produce spore-producing bodies.

In the space provided, write the letter of the term or phrase that best completes each statement or best answers each question.

_____ **5.** Heterotrophic protists can be
   a. autotrophs.
   b. parasites.
   c. detritivores.
   d. All of the above

_____ **6.** Photosynthetic algae are distinguished by the
   a. way they move.
   b. presence or absence of silica shells.
   c. structure of their cell wall.
   d. kind of chlorophyll they contain.

_____ **7.** Chitin, the material found in the hard shells of crabs, insects, and other arthropods, is also found in the cell walls of
   a. ascomycetes.
   b. mushrooms.
   c. bread molds.
   d. All of the above

_____ **8.** All animals have tissues EXCEPT
   a. sponges.
   b. worms.
   c. mollusks.
   d. arthropods.

_____ **9.** Because plants are unable to move, their dispersal depends on
   a. vascular tissue.
   b. roots.
   c. seeds and spores.
   d. leaves.

_____ **10.** Nonvascular plants
  a. are all relatively small.
  b. have fairly complex bodies.
  c. include ferns and flowering plants.
  d. produce seeds in cones.

_____ **11.** Of the 35 phyla that compose the animal kingdom, most occur
  a. in the sea.
  b. on land.
  c. in fresh water.
  d. as vertebrates.

_____ **12.** Gymnosperms are
  a. nonvascular plants.
  b. vascular plants.
  c. nonflowering seed plants.
  d. Both (b) and (c)

_____ **13.** The roles filled by animals in an ecosystem include all of the following EXCEPT
  a. primary consumer.
  b. secondary consumer.
  c. parasite.
  d. primary producer.

Complete each statement by writing the correct term or phrase in the space provided.

14. An organism that is a unicellular prokaryote with a cell wall could be either

a(n) _____ or a(n) _____ .

15. The only kingdom that contains organisms without cell walls is called

_____ .

16. When cells become specialized in form and function, they undergo a process

called _____ .

17. Amoebas move using extensions of cytoplasm called _____ ,

while forams have _____ _____ through which long, thin projections of cytoplasm can be extended.

18. Cells that are permanently associated with one another but that do not

communicate form a(n) _____ _____ .

19. _____ , _____ , and _____
are reproductive structures associated with the three phyla of fungi.

20. Tissues are distinct types of cells with a common _____ and

_____ .

Read each question, and write your answer in the space provided.

21. What is a halophile? To what kingdom does it belong?

_____

_____

_____

22. What four characteristics do biologists use to distinguish between the six kingdoms?

_____

_____

_____

_____

23. Identify the structures produced for reproduction by nonflowering seed plants and seedless vascular plants.

_____

_____

_____

24. What characteristics are common to all vertebrates?

_____

_____

_____

25. Compare the different roles played by plants and animals in most terrestrial food webs.

_____

_____

_____

_____

_____

_____

Viruses and Bacteria

Circle T *if the statement is true or* F *if it is false.*

T F **1.** The envelope of a virus consists of proteins, lipids, and glycoproteins that the virus manufactures.

T F **2.** Although some bacteria are heterotrophic, most are autotrophic.

T F **3.** Antibiotics have been ineffective against some bacteria. These resistant bacteria can pass on their resistance from one generation to the next.

T F **4.** Petroleum-metabolizing bacteria are used to help clean up oil spills.

In the space provided, write the letter of the term or phrase that best completes each statement or best answers each question.

_____ **5.** Tobacco mosaic virus

    a. becomes a crystal when purified.
    b. causes disease in tobacco plants.
    c. is smaller than a bacterium.
    d. All of the above

_____ **6.** Biologists now know that viruses

    a. are the smallest organisms.
    b. consist of a protein surrounded by a nucleic acid coat.
    c. contain RNA or DNA in a protein coat.
    d. all form the same crystalline shape.

_____ **7.** Viruses must rely on host cells for replication because

    a. they need the DNA of the host to replicate.
    b. they lack the enzymes necessary for metabolism and have no structures to make protein.
    c. all viruses are really fragments of host genes and must therefore recombine with a host cell to replicate.
    d. None of the above

_____ **8.** Once inside a cell, HIV is able to produce thousands of new viruses with the help of

    a. specialized prions.
    b. glycoproteins specific to the host cell.
    c. the repeated division of proviruses over time.
    d. the enzyme reverse transcriptase.

_____ **9.** Which of the following comparisons is NOT correct?

	BACTERIA	EUKARYOTES
a.	no cell nucleus	cell nucleus
b.	smaller	larger
c.	circular DNA	linear DNA
d.	mostly aerobic	aerobic and anaerobic

_____ 10. *Escherichia coli* is an example of a bacterium that has short, thin, hairlike appendages called

    a. pili.   **c.** cocci.
    b. cilia.   **d.** ribosomes.

_____ 11. Many gram-negative bacteria have pili, which are used to

    a. aid in the process of binary fission.
    b. propel the bacteria through their environment.
    c. enclose the genetic material of the bacteria.
    d. adhere to surfaces and to join bacterial cells prior to conjugation.

_____ 12. An example of a bacterial disease carried from rodents to humans by fleas is

    a. tuberculosis.   **c.** cholera.
    b. bubonic plague.   **d.** Lyme disease.

Questions 13–15 refer to the figures below, which show different shapes of bacterial cells.

Organism A   Organism B   Organism C

_____ 13. The shape represented by organism *A* is called

    a. coccus.   **c.** bacillus.
    b. spirillum.   **d.** filamentous.

_____ 14. You would expect the bacterial genus *Bacillus* to have the shape of organism

    a. *A*.   **c.** *C*.
    b. *B*.   **d.** None of the above

_____ 15. Which of the organisms above causes AIDS?

    a. organism *A*   **c.** organism *C*
    b. organism *B*   **d.** none of the above

Complete each statement by writing the correct term or phrase in the space provided.

16. Most bacteria are _____ , feeding on organic material formed by other organisms.

17. In some _____ viruses, a change in the environment can

cause the provirus to begin the _____ cycle.

Name_____ Date_____ Class_____

18. One important role of bacteria is the process of _____, in which

bacteria oxidize ammonia into _____ .

19. _____ are protective structures that some bacteria may form under harsh conditions.

20. Bacteria that obtain energy by removing electrons from ammonia,

hydrogen sulfide, or methane are called _____ bacteria.

21. The cycle of viral infection in which the viral genome replicates without

destroying the host cell is called the _____ cycle.

Read each question, and write your answer in the space provided.

22. Viruses are not considered to be living, yet they still have a major impact on the living world. Explain.

_____

_____

_____

23. Antibiotics are generally effective against bacterial infections but cannot be used to treat viral infections. Explain.

_____

_____

_____

24. Describe the importance of the Gram staining technique.

_____

_____

_____

_____

25. Explain how bacterial toxins cause disease.

_____

_____

_____

_____

Copyright © by Holt, Rinehart and Winston. All rights reserved.

Biology: Principles and Explorations **Test** Chapter 21 **63**

CHAPTER
22 **TEST**

Protists

Circle T *if the statement is true or* F *if it is false.*

T   F   **1.** The first protists were prokaryotes.

T   F   **2.** The kingdom Protista contains all eukaryotes that cannot be classified as animals, plants, or fungi.

T   F   **3.** Protists are found in any moist environment except the inside of a living organism.

T   F   **4.** Oomycetes are sometimes called water molds.

T   F   **5.** Amoebic dysentery is usually transmitted from person to person by coughing and sneezing.

In the space provided, write the letter of the term or phrase that best completes each statement or best answers each question.

_____ **6.** Protists get energy by

    a. ingesting food.
    b. absorbing food.
    c. photosynthesis.
    d. All of the above

_____ **7.** The kingdom Protista includes

    a. most of the single-celled eukaryotes.
    b. slime and water molds.
    c. multicellular algae.
    d. All of the above

_____ **8.** Protists thrive

    a. on rocks.
    b. only in damp soil.
    c. only in marine environments.
    d. in water and moist environments.

_____ **9.** Zoospores can be

    a. produced as a result of meiosis.
    b. diploid.
    c. produced as a result of mitosis.
    d. Both (a) and (c)

_____ **10.** In *Chlamydomonas,* the mature zoospores grow to become

    a. mature diploid cells.
    b. mature haploid cells.
    c. a pair of zygospores.
    d. a pair of diploid cells.

_____ **11.** The process of sexual reproduction that involves the side by side alignment of two filaments to exchange nuclear material is called

    a. mitosis.
    b. conjugation.
    c. alternation of generations.
    d. meiosis.

_____ 12. Green algae contain the same pigments found in
  a. sporozoans.   c. plants.
  b. amoebas.   d. paramecia.

_____ 13. A protist that can surround and engulf food particles is most likely a(n)
  a. sporozoan.   c. plasmodial slime mold.
  b. water mold.   d. alga.

_____ 14. During conjugation, two paramecia come together to exchange
  a. enzymes.   c. excess water.
  b. undigested food.   d. haploid micronuclei.

_____ 15. Methods for controlling malaria that do NOT use chemicals include
  a. quinine.   c. mosquito fish.
  b. diatomaceous earth.   d. None of the above

Complete each statement by writing the correct term or phrase in the space provided.

16. Two important features that evolved in protists are sexual reproduction

   and _____ .

17. Diatoms exhibit either radial or _____ symmetry.

18. Protists not only make up much of the _____ in the ocean but

   also are the single largest group of _____ on Earth.

Questions 19–21 refer to the figures below, which show three single-celled organisms.

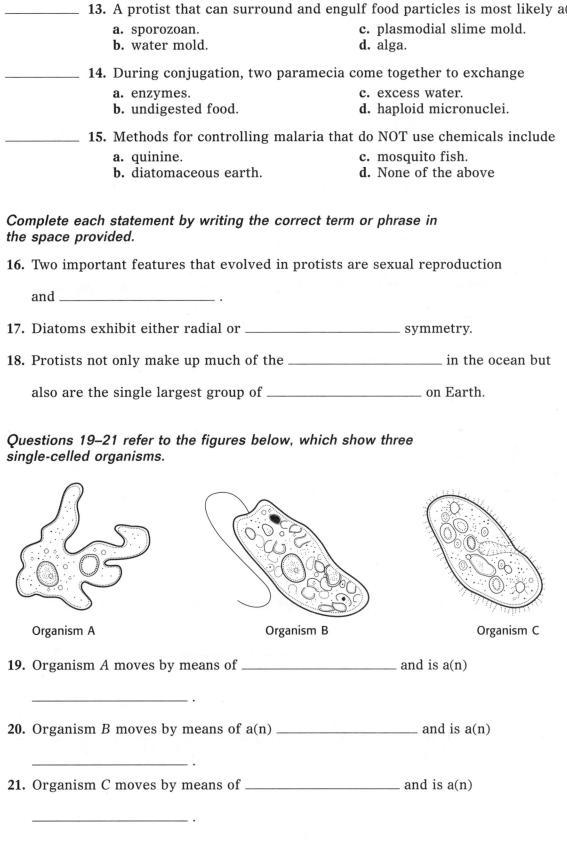

Organism A   Organism B   Organism C

19. Organism *A* moves by means of _____ and is a(n)

   _____ .

20. Organism *B* moves by means of a(n) _____ and is a(n)

   _____ .

21. Organism *C* moves by means of _____ and is a(n)

   _____ .

Read each question, and write your answer in the space provided.

22. List three diseases, other than malaria, that are caused by protists, and explain
how they are transmitted.

_____

_____

_____

_____

_____

_____

23. After a vacation in the tropics, you become seriously ill. Your symptoms
include cycles of chills and fever every 48 hours. Why does your doctor
suspect malaria?

_____

_____

_____

_____

_____

24. Describe three methods used to treat or prevent malaria.

_____

_____

_____

_____

25. Explain how protists can be both beneficial and harmful to humans.

_____

_____

_____

_____

_____

CHAPTER 23 TEST

Fungi

Circle T *if the statement is true or* F *if it is false.*

T F   **1.** Most fungi are heterotrophic, while some are autotrophic.

T F   **2.** Zygosporangia are reproductive structures in which spores form asexually.

T F   **3.** Ringworm is caused by a small wormlike animal.

T F   **4.** Bread molds are characterized by thick-walled sexual structures called zygosporangia.

T F   **5.** In a lichen, the fungus, usually an ascomycete, provides mineral nutrients to the photosynthetic partner.

In the space provided, write the letter of the term or phrase that best completes each statement or best answers each question.

_____ **6.** Fungi play an important role in the biosphere because they
  a. break down organic molecules.
  b. help recycle nutrients.
  c. are decomposers.
  d. All of the above

_____ **7.** The individual filaments that make up the body of a fungus are called
  a. vascular tissue.
  b. hyphae.
  c. rhizoids.
  d. stems.

_____ **8.** Fungi
  a. do not contain chloroplasts.
  b. have cell walls that contain chitin.
  c. do not produce their own food.
  d. All of the above

_____ **9.** In both phylum Ascomycota and phylum Basidiomycota,
  a. sexual spores form in basidia.
  b. hyphae are divided by walls.
  c. sexual spores form in asci.
  d. the mycelia are called stolons.

_____ **10.** *Amanita muscaria* has
  a. cell walls made of chitin.
  b. club-shaped reproductive cells called asci.
  c. the polysaccharide cellulose.
  d. All of the above

_____ **11.** Fungi are used to
  a. produce antibiotics.   **c.** flavor cheese.
  b. ferment soy sauce.   **d.** All of the above

_____ 12. Mycorrhizae
   a. aid in the transfer of minerals from the soil to a plant.
   b. cause a variety of plant diseases.
   c. aid in the transfer of minerals to fungi.
   d. are found only on aquatic fungi.

Questions 13–15 refer to the figure below, which shows the life cycle of a mold.

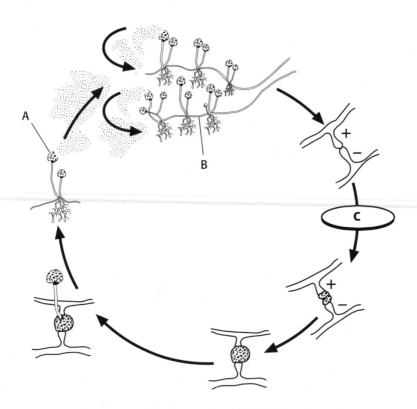

_____ 13. The structure labeled *A* produces
   a. asci.   c. rhizoids.
   b. haploid spores.   d. stolons.

_____ 14. The structure labeled *B* is
   a. a rhizoid.   c. a stolon.
   b. vascular tissue.   d. a stem.

_____ 15. The process that takes place at stage *C* is known as
   a. meiosis.   c. mitosis.
   b. conjugation.   d. fusion.

Complete each statement by writing the correct term or phrase in the space provided.

16. Fungi obtain food by _____ organic matter in dead or living organisms.

17. Asexual reproduction is rare among the _____ .

18. A fungal _____ is a haploid reproductive cell that is capable of developing into a new organism.

19. A(n) _____ is a saclike structure in which haploid spores are formed.

20. A _____ of a fungus, made of a tangled mass of

    _____ , is usually hidden within the substrate on which the fungus is growing.

21. Some fungi in phylum Ascomycota, the _____ , do not have any sexual reproduction structures.

22. The structures produced during sexual reproduction that distinguish the three

    phyla of fungi are _____ , _____ , and

    _____ .

Read each question, and write your answer in the space provided.

23. Both mycorrhizae and lichens have symbiotic relationships. Describe how they differ from one another.

    _____

    _____

    _____

    _____

    _____

    _____

24. Why are fungi well suited for absorbing food from the environment?

    _____

    _____

    _____

25. How did mycorrhizae help plants invade the land?

    _____

    _____

    _____

CHAPTER
(24) TEST

Introduction to Plants

Circle T *if the statement is true or* F *if it is false.*

T F **1.** The sporophyte of a nonvascular plant is larger than the gametophyte.

T F **2.** Plants probably evolved from unicellular aquatic brown algae that could not survive on land.

T F **3.** Ferns need water to reproduce because their sperm must swim to eggs.

T F **4.** Flowers permit cross-pollination between individuals that live far apart.

T F **5.** One advantage of seed dispersal is that it prevents competition between parents and offspring.

In the space provided, write the letter of the term or phrase that best completes each statement or best answers each question.

_____ **6.** The cuticle is a waxy covering that covers
   a. nonwoody aboveground plant parts.
   b. flowers.
   c. seeds.
   d. nonwoody belowground plant parts.

_____ **7.** The xylem in a plant transports
   a. food from the leaves.
   b. water and minerals.
   c. organic nutrients.
   d. All of the above

_____ **8.** In mosses, sporophytes grow from the tip of a
   a. meristem.   **c.** cone.
   b. spore capsule.   **d.** gametophyte.

_____ **9.** The gametophytes of nonvascular plants are anchored to surfaces by
   a. roots.   **c.** mycorrhizae.
   b. sporophytes.   **d.** rhizoids.

_____ **10.** The primary function of a fruit is
   a. to provide nutrition for the seed.   **c.** seed dispersal.
   b. photosynthesis.   **d.** to permit cross-fertilization.

_____ **11.** Which of the following plant parts can be eaten as food?
   a. stem   **c.** fruit
   b. roots   **d.** all of the above

_____ **12.** Which of the following identifies a fiber source and its use?
   a. cotton—clothing   **c.** hemp and sisal—rope
   b. flax—linen   **d.** all of the above

Name_____ Date _____ Class _____

Questions 13–15 refer to the figure below, which shows the life cycle of a plant.

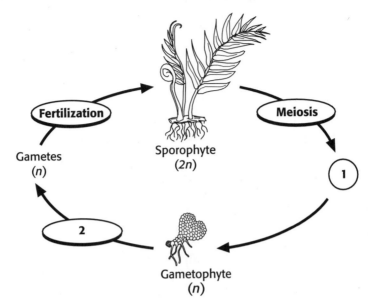

_____ **13.** The life cycle shown in the figure above is called alternation of generations because it alternates a
  a. haploid gametophyte and a diploid sporophyte.
  b. diploid gametophyte and a haploid sporophyte.
  c. haploid gametophyte and a haploid sporophyte.
  d. diploid sporophyte and a haploid sporophyte.

_____ **14.** The structures produced at stage 1 are
  a. spore capsules.   **c.** haploid spores.
  b. diploid spores.   **d.** zygotes.

_____ **15.** What process occurs at stage 2 to produce the gametes?
  a. fertilization   **c.** meiosis
  b. pollination   **d.** mitosis

Complete each statement by writing the correct term or phrase in the space provided.

16. On the surface of leaves, guard cells regulate the opening and closing of the

_____ by changing shape.

17. Seeds _____ and _____ the plant embryo.

18. The life cycle of seed plants is characterized by very tiny

_____ .

19. Root crops are a source of _____ , while,

_____ are a good source of protein.

Name _____ Date _____ Class _____

Questions 20–22 refer to the figure at right, which shows the parts of a seed.

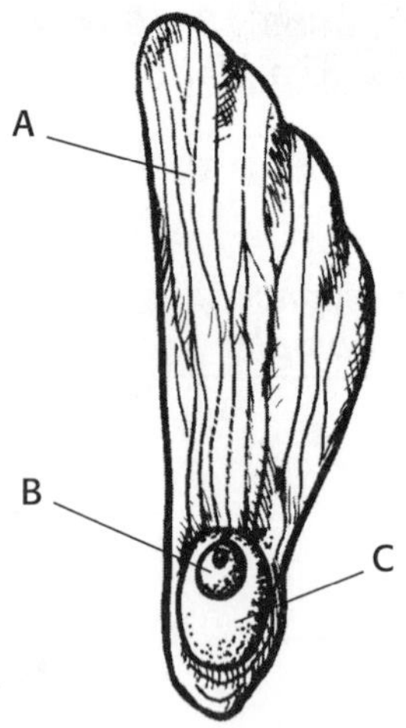

20. The structure labeled *A* is called a(n) _____ ,

    which aids in _____ .

21. The structure labeled *B* is the _____ ,
    which is an early stage in development.

22. The structure labeled *C* contains _____

    _____ , which provides nourishment to the
    embryo as it starts to grow.

A

B

C

Read each question, and write your answer in the space provided.

23. Describe 4 of the 12 phyla of plants. Give an example of a plant that belongs
    in each phylum.

    _____

    _____

    _____

    _____

    _____

    _____

24. Describe how certain characteristics of flowers promote pollination.

    _____

    _____

    _____

    _____

    _____

    _____

25. Trace the development of aspirin.

    _____

    _____

    _____

    _____

CHAPTER

25 **TEST**

Plant Reproduction

In the space provided, write the letter of the term or phrase that best completes each statement or best answers each question.

_____ 1. The gametophyte is much larger than the sporophyte in

    a. conifers.   **c.** horsetails.

    b. ferns.   **d.** liverworts.

_____ 2. Mosses and ferns are alike in that they can reproduce sexually only when

    a. a film of water covers the gametophyte.

    b. a film of water covers the sporophyte.

    c. the gametophytes germinate.

    d. the sporophytes are small.

_____ 3. The seed part that protects the embryo from mechanical injury and keeps out water and oxygen is called the

    a. sorus.   **c.** seed coat.

    b. cotyledon.   **d.** ovule.

_____ 4. In gymnosperms, gametophytes form on

    a. flowers.   **c.** stamens.

    b. the scales of cones.   **d.** the scales of sepals.

_____ 5. In the life cycle of a pine tree,

    a. both male and female cones are produced.

    b. seeds with wings travel away from the parent tree.

    c. microscopic gametophytes develop from spores.

    d. All of the above

_____ 6. A zygote and endosperm are produced in the process called

    a. alternation of generations.   **c.** double fertilization.

    b. meiosis.   **d.** vegetative propagation.

_____ 7. Mosses and ferns have

    a. haploid sporophytes, haploid spores, and diploid gametophytes.

    b. diploid sporophytes, haploid spores, and haploid gametophytes.

    c. haploid sporophytes, diploid spores, and haploid gametophytes.

    d. diploid sporophytes, haploid spores, and diploid gametophytes.

_____ 8. The tiny seeds produced by kalanchoë flowers result from

    a. asexual reproduction.   **c.** sexual reproduction.

    b. vegetative reproduction.   **d.** tissue culture.

_____ 9. Which of the following is NOT a method of vegetative plant propagation?

    a. grafting   **c.** cuttings

    b. seeds   **d.** tissue culture

Name_____ Date _____ Class _____

Questions 10–14 refer to the figure at right, which shows the structure of a flower.

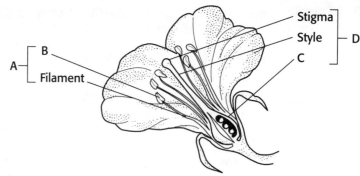

_____ **10.** The structure labeled *B* produces
    a. male gametophytes.   **c.** female gametophytes.
    b. seeds.   **d.** antheridia.

_____ **11.** Which of the following occurs during pollination?
    a. Pollen grains from *B* are transferred to *C.*
    b. Eggs from *C* are transferred to *B.*
    c. Eggs from *B* are transferred to *D.*
    d. Pollen grains from *A* are transferred to *D.*

_____ **12.** The pollen-producing sac is part of the structure labeled
    a. *A.*   **c.** *C.*
    b. *B.*   **d.** *D.*

_____ **13.** In angiosperms, ovules are produced in the structure labeled
    a. *A.*   **c.** *C.*
    b. *B.*   **d.** *D.*

_____ **14.** An imperfect flower is a flower that lacks structure
    a. *A* or *B.*   **c.** *A* or *C.*
    b. *A* or *D.*   **d.** *B* or *C.*

Complete each statement by writing the correct term or phrase in the space provided.

15. In a flower, female _____ develop in ovules within the ovary,

which is the lower portion of the _____ .

16. In seed plants, sperm that develop within _____

_____ travel to the egg within a(n) _____

through a(n) _____ _____ .

17. A leaflike structure of a seed that transfers nutrients to the embryo is called

a(n) _____ .

18. Angiosperm flowers have four basic types of parts—the _____ ,

the _____ , the _____ , and the

_____ .

19. In angiosperm reproduction, the zygote and the tissues of the ovule develop

into a(n) _____ , which grows into a new _____ .

20. Plant propagation is the process of growing new plants from

_____ or _____ _____ .

Read each question, and write your answer in the space provided.

21. Beginning with the sporophyte stage, describe the life cycle of a fern.

_____

_____

_____

_____

_____

22. Describe how sperm reach eggs in a conifer.

_____

_____

_____

_____

23. What happens after a pollen tube is formed in angiosperms?

_____

_____

_____

_____

24. List five examples of stuctures by which plants reproduce asexually.

_____

_____

_____

25. Describe how plantlets are involved in the reproduction of kalanchoës.

_____

_____

_____

CHAPTER
26 **TEST**

Plant Structure and Function

Circle T *if the statement is true or* F *if it is false.*

T   F   **1.** Ground tissue surrounds and supports the vascular tissue of a plant.

T   F   **2.** Maple flowers develop several weeks after the leaves appear.

T   F   **3.** Sugars and starches are stored in roots.

T   F   **4.** The water taken in by roots replaces the water lost through transpiration.

Questions 5 and 6 refer to the figure below, which shows the structure of a leaf.

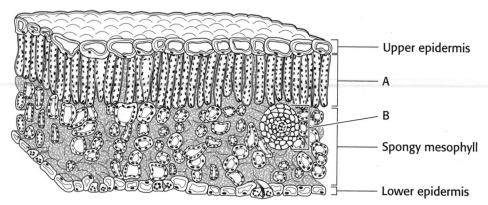

T   F   **5.** The structure labeled *A* is a portion of the leaf mesophyll and is located directly below the upper epidermis.

T   F   **6.** The structure labeled *B* is a part of the mesophyll and contains cells that conduct photosynthesis.

In the space provided, write the letter of the term or phrase that best completes each statement or best answers each question.

_____ **7.** Depending on the type of plant or plant part, the dermal tissue is
     a. xylem or phloem.   **c.** cork or epidermis.
     b. heartwood or sapwood.   **d.** mesophyll or xylem.

_____ **8.** Which of the following is NOT a characteristic of herbaceous stems?
     a. They are covered by cork.
     b. They are flexible.
     c. The vascular tissue is arranged in bundles.
     d. They are usually green.

_____ **9.** The primary function of root hairs is
     a. support.   **c.** absorption of water and minerals.
     b. transport of food.   **d.** water storage.

_____ **10.** Transpiration is the process by which

      a. plants reproduce.

      b. food is transported.

      c. seeds are produced.

      d. water is lost by a plant.

_____ **11.** Leaves can be referred to as being either

      a. woody or herbaceous.

      b. fibrous or adventitious.

      c. vascular or nonvascular.

      d. simple or compound.

_____ **12.** The seeds of the sugar maple mature inside fruits that are carried away by

      a. squirrels.

      b. birds.

      c. the wind.

      d. pollinators.

_____ **13.** Which of the following is NOT a type of tissue in vascular plants?

      a. ground tissue

      b. xylem

      c. dermal tissue

      d. cuticle

_____ **14.** The cork of a woody stem

      a. conducts water.

      b. prevents physical damage and water loss.

      c. aids in transpiration.

      d. aids in photosynthesis.

_____ **15.** In translocation, organic compounds move

      a. through phloem.

      b. through living cells.

      c. from leaves and roots.

      d. All of the above

Complete each statement by writing the correct term or phrase in the space provided.

16. Garden-pea tendrils are _____ _____ specialized for climbing.

17. In sugar maples, the sugary sap comes from the _____ .

18. Specialized functions of potato stems are _____

_____ and _____ _____ .

19. Photosynthesis takes place in the _____ cells, which make up

a leaf's _____ tissue.

20. The diffusion of water vapor through the _____ of a leaf is

called _____ .

21. In herbaceous dicot stems, bundles of _____ and

_____ , called vascular bundles, are arranged in a(n)

_____ .

22. The _____ _____ of a leaf contains large

_____ _____ through which gases can travel.

Read each question, and write your answer in the space provided.

23. Describe how stomata open and close.

_____

_____

_____

_____

_____

24. Define the terms *source* and *sink* in relation to the translocation of organic compounds in the phloem of plants. Give examples of each.

_____

_____

_____

_____

_____

25. Summarize the pressure-flow model of translocation.

_____

_____

_____

_____

_____

_____

_____

CHAPTER

27 **TEST**

Plant Growth and Development

Circle T *if the statement is true or* F *if it is false.*

T F **1.** Secondary tissues result from cell division in apical meristems.

T F **2.** Plant development is considered reversible because cells of certain tissues can form unspecialized cells that can then differentiate and develop into a mature plant.

T F **3.** Herbaceous annuals, such as chrysanthemums, store nutrients for the next season's growth in fleshy roots or underground stems.

T F **4.** The shoot of a corn seedling grows straight up, whereas a bean seedling produces a shoot with a hook to push through the soil.

T F **5.** Short-day plants flower when nights are long.

In the space provided, write the letter of the term or phrase that best completes each statement or best answers each question.

_____ **6.** Like other grasses, a wheat plant is characterized by having
  a. a fibrous root system.
  b. flowers that lack petals and sepals.
  c. apical meristems that rise from a point near the surface of the soil.
  d. All of the above

_____ **7.** Which of the following may be needed in order for a seed to germinate?
  a. rising temperature
  b. exposure to cold
  c. penetration of water and oxygen through the seed coat
  d. all of the above

_____ **8.** A plant that completes its life cycle in a single growing season is called a(n)
  a. annual.   **c.** biennial.
  b. perennial.   **d.** perpetual.

_____ **9.** Which of the following is a list of three major mineral nutrients required by plants?
  a. magnesium, sulfur, and carbon dioxide
  b. nitrogen, phosphorus, and potassium
  c. potassium, water, and magnesium
  d. nitrogen, oxygen, and sulfur

_____ **10.** A plant's roots
  a. generally protrude into the air to absorb oxygen.
  b. produce oxygen during photosynthesis.
  c. obtain oxygen from air spaces between soil particles.
  d. carry out photosynthesis.

_____ 11. Cells on the dark side of a stem elongate more than the cells on the light side because the hormone
   a. ethylene inhibits the cells on the light side.
   b. ethylene stimulates cell growth on the dark side.
   c. auxin accumulates on the dark side and causes the cell walls to become more flexible.
   d. auxin accumulates on the light side and causes the cell walls to become less flexible.

_____ 12. When vines grow, their tendrils coil around objects for support. This action is called a
   a. phototropism.
   b. gravitropism.
   c. thigmotropism.
   d. photoperiodism.

_____ 13. When commercial growers artificially control the lengths of days and nights, they are relying on a response called a
   a. photoperiodism.
   b. phototropism.
   c. thigmotropism.
   d. gravitropism.

Questions 14 and 15 refer to the figure below, which shows a seedling.

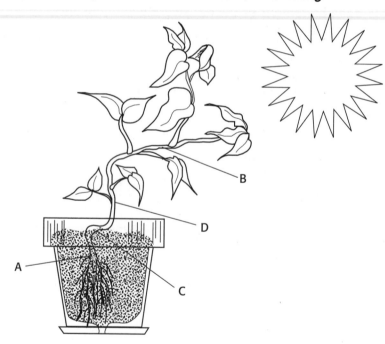

_____ 14. Which part of the plant exhibits a positive phototropism?
   a. A
   b. B
   c. C
   d. D

_____ 15. Which part of the plant exhibits a positive gravitropism?
   a. A
   b. B
   c. C
   d. D

Complete each statement by writing the correct term or phrase in the space provided.

16. Resumption of growth by a plant embryo is called _____ .

17. Regions of a plant in which growth occurs by active cell division are called

_____ .

18. The process by which cells become specialized in form and function is called

_____ .

19. _____ meristems produce primary growth, and in woody

plants, two meristems called the _____ cambium and the

_____ cambium produce secondary growth.

20. Although the availability of light and nutrients affects the rate of plant growth, many of a plant's responses to environmental stimuli are triggered by

_____ .

21. The inhibition of the growth of buds along a stem by the

hormone _____ is called apical dominance.

22. The condition in which a plant or seed remains inactive is called

_____ .

23. Unlike development in animals, development in plants is _____

and _____ .

Read each question, and write your answer in the space provided.

24. Secondary growth adds width to a woody stem. Briefly describe the tissues involved, and explain how they increase the stem's width.

_____

_____

_____

_____

25. Describe the stems, roots, and grain structure of bread wheat.

_____

_____

_____

_____

Introduction to Animals

Circle T *if the statement is true or* F *if it is false.*

T   F   **1.** The common ancestor of animals was probably a unicellular protist with a flagellum.

T   F   **2.** The development of a true coelom within the mesoderm aided the evolution of complex organs.

T   F   **3.** The exchange of oxygen and carbon dioxide gas during respiration can only occur on a wet surface, such as that found in lungs.

T   F   **4.** Segmentation limits evolutionary flexibility.

T   F   **5.** The embryos of humans do not show blastula formation.

In the space provided, write the letter of the term or phrase that best completes each statement or best answers each question.

_____ **6.** An obvious characteristic of animals that distinguishes them from the members of the other kingdoms is that animals
   a. are capable of more complex and rapid movements than members of the other kingdoms.
   b. have cells with rigid cell walls.
   c. have organs but no tissues.
   d. include both aquatic and terrestrial species.

_____ **7.** In segmented worms, a segment
   a. can contain the same kinds of organs as an adjacent segment.
   b. can be modified for feeding or reproduction.
   c. is connected to a brain by nerves.
   d. All of the above

_____ **8.** A true coelom
   a. becomes the cavity within the digestive tract.
   b. develops between the mesoderm and the endoderm.
   c. is located between the ectoderm and the mesoderm.
   d. develops completely within the mesoderm.

_____ **9.** All animals except sponges exhibit
   a. heterotrophy, cephalization, and sexual reproduction.
   b. mobility, symmetry, and diploidy.
   c. blastula formation, tissues, and symmetry.
   d. tissues, cell walls, and heterotrophy.

_____ **10.** Scientists studying the evolutionary relationships of living animals might compare the animals'
   a. DNA and embryonic development.
   b. anatomy, and they might study fossils of the species.
   c. physiology.
   d. All of the above

_____ **11.** Asexual reproduction
   a. involves the mass release of gametes.
   b. does not require an egg and sperm.
   c. requires internal fertilization.
   d. is used by earthworms and slugs.

_____ **12.** Ganglia are
   a. clusters of nerve nets.   **c.** clusters of neurons.
   b. primitive nerve cells.   **d.** None of the above

_____ **13.** In acoelomates, the space between the body wall and the gut is filled with
   a. cells from the mesoderm.
   b. fluid.
   c. cells from the mesoderm and the endoderm.
   d. muscle tissue.

Questions 14 and 15 refer to the figure below.

Organism A   **Organism B**

_____ **14.** The position of the arrow next to organism A can be referred to as
   a. posterior.   **c.** dorsal.
   b. anterior.   **d.** ventral.

_____ **15.** Organism B is
   a. radially symmetrical.   **c.** unilaterally symmetrical.
   b. bilaterally symmetrical.   **d.** nonsymmetrical.

Complete each statement by writing the correct term or phrase in the space provided.

16. Because animals cannot make their own food, they are said to be

_____ .

17. Animals with a one-way digestive tract have a(n) _____ and

a(n) _____ .

18. Animals that have their body parts arranged around a central point are said

to exhibit _____ _____ .

19. The skeletal system supports an animal's body, is essential for

_____ , and helps protect the animal's soft tissues.

20. The evolution of a definite head end of an organism is called

_____ .

21. A(n) _____ is a collection of different types of cells that work together to perform a particular function.

22. In a(n) _____ _____ , all cells participate in all stages of food digestion.

Read each question, and write your answer in the space provided.

23. Distinguish between open and closed circulatory systems.

_____

_____

_____

_____

_____

_____

24. Explain an evolutionary benefit of bilateral symmetry.

_____

_____

_____

_____

_____

25. How does the presence of digestive enzymes affect an animal's diet?

_____

_____

_____

_____

_____

CHAPTER
(29) **TEST**

Simple Invertebrates

Circle T *if the statement is true or* F *if it is false.*

T F   **1.** Sponges are filter feeders.

T F   **2.** Some sponges are capable of total regeneration, even from the smallest pieces of their bodies.

T F   **3.** Tapeworms absorb food from their host's intestine directly through their skin.

T F   **4.** Humans can avoid trichinosis by wearing shoes when they walk through fields.

T F   **5.** Planarians have a branched digestive tract with both a mouth and an anus.

In the space provided, write the letter of the term or phrase that best completes each statement or best answers each question.

_____   **6.** Water leaves the internal cavity of a sponge through the
    a. food vacuoles.   **c.** mesoglea.
    b. spicules.   **d.** oscula.

_____   **7.** Skeletal support in sponges may be provided by
    a. spicules of calcium carbonate.
    b. spicules of silica.
    c. spongin fibers.
    d. All of the above

_____   **8.** The class of cnidarians that has no medusa stage is
    a. Anthozoa.   **c.** Scyphozoa.
    b. Hydrozoa.   **d.** None of the above

_____   **9.** Anthozoans include organisms known as
    a. jellyfish.   **c.** the Portuguese men-of-war.
    b. hydras.   **d.** sea anemones and corals.

_____   **10.** Flatworms have no need for circulatory and respiratory systems because
    a. the digestive system performs these functions.
    b. their cells are close to the animal's exterior surface.
    c. the spherical body shape allows diffusion of materials into tissues.
    d. the coelom is bathed in blood and oxygen.

_____   **11.** A type of roundworm that lives a parasitic life is
    a. *Ascaris.*   **c.** *Trichinella.*
    b. *Necator.*   **d.** All of the above

_____   **12.** Which of the following statements about tapeworms is false?
    a. They can infect a person who eats improperly cooked beef.
    b. They belong to the genus *Schistosoma.*
    c. They can grow large in human intestines.
    d. They do not have a digestive system.

Questions 13–15 refer to the figure below, which shows the life cycle of the common jellyfish Aurelia.

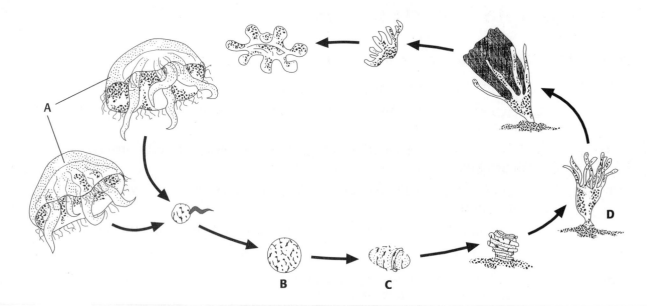

_____ 13. The structure labeled *C*
   a. results from the fertilization of eggs by sperm.
   b. swims freely through the water.
   c. settles at the ocean bottom and grows into polyps.
   d. All of the above

_____ 14. Which structure(s) reproduce sexually?
   a. *A*
   b. *D*
   c. both (a) and (b)
   d. none of the above

_____ 15. Which structure(s) reproduce asexually?
   a. *A*   **c.** both (a) and (b)
   b. *D*   **d.** none of the above

Complete each statement by writing the correct term or phrase in the space provided.

16. Facing into the internal cavity of a sponge are flagellated collar cells called

   _____ .

17. Freshwater sponges protect themselves during harsh weather by forming a(n)

   _____ , a structure that encloses amoebocytes in a protective
   covering until conditions are more favorable.

18. An organism that produces both eggs and sperm is called a(n)

   _____ .

19. The _____ is a thick, protective cellular covering of the bodies of endoparasitic flukes that prevents them from being digested by their hosts.

20. Tapeworms grow by producing a string of rectangular body segments called

_____ . Each segment is a complete reproductive unit.

Read each question, and write your answer in the space provided.

21. Explain how cnidocytes and nematocysts function.

_____

_____

_____

22. Roundworms are characterized by a pseudocoelom. Explain how a pseudocoelom functions.

_____

_____

_____

23. Distinguish between a polyp and a medusa. Give an example of each.

_____

_____

_____

24. Suppose you were asked to make a poster about things people can do to protect themselves from parasites. What warnings and advice would you include in your poster? List at least three pieces of advice.

_____

_____

_____

_____

_____

25. Describe the specialized features of the Portuguese man-of-war.

_____

_____

_____

_____

CHAPTER
30 **TEST**

Mollusks and Annelids

Circle T *if the statement is true or* F *if it is false.*

T F **1.** Mollusks and annelids are thought to have been the first major group of organisms to develop a true coelom.

T F **2.** Mollusks must eat constantly because their nephridia dispose of useful molecules as well as waste products.

T F **3.** Because cephalopods have tentacles, they have no need for a radula.

T F **4.** While all but one group of mollusks have open circulatory systems, all annelids have a closed circulatory system.

In the space provided, write the letter of the term or phrase that best completes each statement or best answers each question.

_____ **5.** All of the following are characteristics of mollusks EXCEPT
    a. a pseudocoelomate body plan.   **c.** a complete digestive tract.
    b. bilateral symmetry.   **d.** an open circulatory system.

_____ **6.** In annelids, a significant evolutionary change in body plan is
    a. the ability to burrow.   **c.** segmentation.
    b. the existence of a true coelom.   **d.** bilateral symmetry.

_____ **7.** The advantage of a closed circulatory system over an open circulatory system is that
    a. blood moves more efficiently through the tubes of a closed circulatory system.
    b. a closed circulatory system prevents blood from leaking out of the body.
    c. blood can be pumped by a muscular heart in a closed circulatory system.
    d. lungs can function in animals with a closed circulatory system.

_____ **8.** In order to digest the nutrients in soil, earthworms must
    a. have nephridia to filter out nutrients.
    b. grind the soil in their gizzard.
    c. coordinate muscular activity in each body segment.
    d. have a hydrostatic skeleton.

_____ **9.** Polychaetes, or marine worms, may have parapodia, which
    a. are fleshy, paddlelike structures.
    b. greatly increase the surface area of the animal's body.
    c. usually have setae and are used in movement.
    d. All of the above

_____ **10.** Oysters and other bivalves form pearls when
    a. minerals are filtered from water circulating through them.
    b. sand becomes lodged between their mantle and shell.
    c. contaminants in polluted water circulate through them.
    d. pieces of their shell break off, irritating their visceral mass.

Name_____ Date _____ Class _____

_____ **11.** Earthworms must stay moist because they
      a. absorb nutrients through skin.   **c.** respire through skin.
      b. lose moisture through skin.   **d.** None of the above

_____ **12.** Bivalves open and close their valves by
      a. contracting and relaxing the adductor muscles.
      b. drawing sea water in through a siphon.
      c. expelling water from their shell.
      d. means of sensory cells along the edge of their valves.

Questions 13–15 refer to the figure below, which shows a typical mollusk.

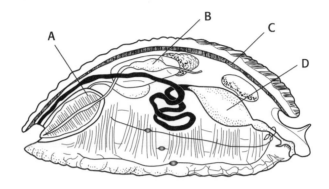

_____ **13.** The structure involved with respiration is labeled
      a. *A.*   **c.** *C.*
      b. *B.*   **d.** *D.*

_____ **14.** The structure called the mantle is labeled
      a. *A.*   **c.** *C.*
      b. *B.*   **d.** *D.*

_____ **15.** The structure used to collect waste-laden fluids is labeled
      a. *A.*   **c.** *C.*
      b. *B.*   **d.** *D.*

Complete each statement by writing the correct term or phrase in the space provided.

16. The _____ larva is a distinguishing characteristic of mollusks and annelids.

17. Constant beating of _____ in the mantle cavity of mollusks causes a continuous stream of water to pass over the gills.

18. Water is drawn into the body of bivalves through tubes called _____ .

19. Annelids have a(n) _____ _____ , which is a primitive brain.

20. In annelids, _____ divide body segments, while

_____ help the animal move from place to place.

Biology: Principles and Explorations **Test** Chapter 30   **89**

Copyright © by Holt, Rinehart and Winston. All rights reserved.

Read each question, and write your answer in the space provided.

21. Describe the function of the visceral mass, the mantle, and the foot in mollusks.

_____

_____

_____

_____

22. Distinguish between the three classes of annelids.

_____

_____

_____

_____

_____

23. Explain why cephalopods are considered the most intelligent of all invertebrates. Give at least two reasons.

_____

_____

_____

_____

24. Explain how squid and octopuses can move quickly to escape danger.

_____

_____

_____

25. Explain why earthworms are beneficial to agriculture.

_____

_____

_____

31 TEST

Arthropods

Circle T *if the statement is true or* F *if it is false.*

T   F   **1.** Like annelids, arthropods have segmented appendages.

T   F   **2.** Insects were the first animals to develop wings.

T   F   **3.** Grasshoppers have three light-detecting antennae.

T   F   **4.** A protective shield called a carapace protects the back of a decapod.

In the space provided, write the letter of the term or phrase that best completes each statement or best answers each question.

_____ **5.** The appendages that scorpions and spiders use to capture and handle their prey are called

    a. diptera.   **c.** pedipalps.
    b. walking legs.   **d.** uropods.

_____ **6.** Malpighian tubules in insects

    a. remove wastes.   **c.** carry Malpighian fluid.
    b. carry blood.   **d.** are important in respiration.

_____ **7.** The ovipositors of a grasshopper

    a. are used to deposit ovaries.   **c.** contain developing ovaries.
    b. incubate eggs.   **d.** are used to dig holes.

_____ **8.** The structures on a spider's abdomen that direct the flow of silk from silk-producing glands are called

    a. spiracles.   **c.** chelicerates.
    b. pedipalps.   **d.** spinnerets.

_____ **9.** The horseshoe crab is

    a. a common garden pest in the northeastern United States.
    b. found in large freshwater lakes.
    c. not really a crab.
    d. the direct ancestor of echinoderms.

_____ **10.** Which of the following is a characteristic of the brown recluse spider?

    a. It has book lungs.
    b. It has poison glands connected to fanged chelicera.
    c. It has a violin-shaped mark on its cephalothorax.
    d. all of the above

_____ **11.** Which of the following is NOT a subphylum of arthropods?

    a. Chelicerata   **c.** Crustacea
    b. Uniramia   **d.** Insecta

_____ **12.** In complete metamorphosis, the larva develops into an adult during the

    a. nymph stage.   **c.** growth stage.
    b. pupa stage.   **d.** molt stage.

_____ 13. The correct sequence of events during complete metamorphosis is
   a. egg, larva, chrysalis, and adult.
   b. egg, larva, nymph, and adult.
   c. egg, nymph, larva, and adult.
   d. egg, larva, pupa, and adult.

_____ 14. Insect wings are an outgrowth of
   a. a network of chitin.
   b. the body wall of the thorax.
   c. the body wall of the abdomen.
   d. the cephalothorax.

Complete each statement by writing the correct term or phrase in the space provided.

15. Arthropods such as centipedes have jaws called _____ .

16. Mites, including chiggers and ticks, have bodies in which the

_____ , _____ , and _____
are fused into a single body.

17. The largest group of organisms on Earth is the _____ .

Questions 18–20 refer to the figure below, which shows the internal structure of a spider.

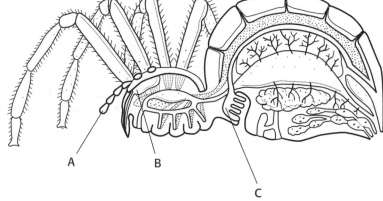

18. During mating, the male spider uses the structure labeled *A*, called

_____ , to insert sperm into the female.

19. The structure labeled *B*, called the _____

_____ , releases venom.

20. _____ _____ , labeled *C*, contain stacks of
thin, blood-filled plates of tissue through which blood picks up oxygen.

Read each question, and write your answer in the space provided.

21. If a mutation that would prevent molting occurred during a grasshopper's embryonic development, how might the grasshopper be affected?

_____

_____

_____

_____

22. Describe three major characteristics of the crustaceans called decapods.

_____

_____

_____

_____

_____

23. Explain how an arthropod's exoskeleton and muscles work together to enable the animal to move.

_____

_____

_____

_____

_____

24. Describe five distinctive characteristics of class Chelicerata.

_____

_____

_____

_____

25. Describe the distinctive thorax of insects.

_____

_____

_____

Echinoderms and Invertebrate Chordates

Circle T *if the statement is true or* F *if it is false.*

T F **1.** The structures that develop from the blastopore define an organism as being either a protostome or a deuterostome.

T F **2.** Echinoderms and chordates are both deuterostomes. They are also both radially symmetrical.

T F **3.** In most echinoderms, the ossicles bear spines that project upward through the skin.

T F **4.** The evolution of an endoskeleton was important to the evolution of vertebrates.

T F **5.** Most chordates are invertebrates.

In the space provided, write the letter of the term or phrase that best completes each statement or best answers each question.

_____ **6.** The first deuterostomes
  a. were probably tunicates.
  b. evolved more than 650 million years ago.
  c. evolved in the last 65 million years.
  d. probably lived in fresh water.

_____ **7.** Although the tube feet of echinoderms serve to move them across the seafloor, tube feet also
  a. aid in gas exchange and waste excretion.
  b. serve as reproductive organs.
  c. serve as the primary circulatory system.
  d. All of the above

_____ **8.** Wastes that accumulate in skin gills of echinoderms are
  a. released into the surrounding water.
  b. reabsorbed into the echinoderm's system.
  c. filtered by pharyngeal slits.
  d. None of the above

_____ **9.** Pedicellaria
  a. may contain toxins.
  b. are pincerlike structures.
  c. have their own muscles and nerves.
  d. All of the above

_____ **10.** Chordate characteristics can be observed in
  a. annelids and echinoderms.
  b. arthropods and annelids.
  c. echinoderms and vertebrates.
  d. lancelets and tunicates.

_____ **11.** Chordates tend to grow larger and move more quickly than other animals because they
  a. reproduce more often.
  b. have an endoskeleton with muscles attached to it.
  c. have a tail that provides added balance.
  d. All of the above

_____ **12.** Invertebrate chordates are so named because they have
  a. a notochord but no backbone.
  b. no notochord nor backbone.
  c. a notochord and a backbone.
  d. no notochord but do have a backbone.

_____ **13.** During embryonic development in vertebrates, the notochord is replaced by a(n)
  a. endoskeleton.   **c.** flexible rod.
  b. vertebral column. **d.** nerve cord.

Questions 14 and 15 refer to the figure below.

_____ **14.** The structure labeled *A* is a
  a. notochord.   **c.** pharynx.
  b. dorsal nerve cord. **d.** tail.

_____ **15.** The organism in the figure above is a(n)
  a. invertebrate chordate.   **c.** hermaphrodite as an adult.
  b. freshwater organism.   **d.** vertebrate chordate.

Complete each statement by writing the correct term or phrase in the space provided.

16. The majority of chordate species have a(n) _____ .

17. The word *deuterostome* comes from the Greek words *deuteros*, meaning

_____ , and *stoma*, meaning _____ .

18. A sea star can use its _____ _____ to pull a bivalve open.

19. As larvae, all echinoderms are _____ symmetrical, but as adults,

they become _____ symmetrical.

20. The only chordate characteristics that are retained in the adult tunicate is (are)

the _____ _____ .

Read each question, and write your answer in the space provided.

21. Explain how the sea star's water vascular system functions.

_____

_____

22. Explain the developmental patterns of protostomes and deuterostomes. Give
at least two examples of each.

_____

_____

_____

23. Summarize the characteristics of echinoderms.

_____

_____

_____

_____

_____

_____

24. Explain why humans are classified as chordates.

_____

_____

_____

_____

25. Briefly describe how a tunicate eats.

_____

_____

_____

CHAPTER

33 **TEST**

Introduction to Vertebrates

Circle T *if the statement is true or* F *if it is false.*

T F **1.** All vertebrates have bilateral symmetry, simple brains, and an open circulatory system.

T F **2.** The first vertebrates were fish that had neither jaws nor paired fins.

T F **3.** Amphibians probably evolved from lobe-finned fishes.

T F **4.** Reptiles must seek out water or damp areas to reproduce.

T F **5.** One factor that affected dinosaur evolution was the movement of the continents.

T F **6.** Egg-laying mammals were the first group of mammals to evolve.

In the space provided, write the letter of the term or phrase that best completes each statement or best answers each question.

_____ **7.** Mammals were most likely descendants of early reptiles called
    a. thecodonts.   **c.** therapsids.
    b. agnathans.   **d.** lampreys.

_____ **8.** Which of the following features helped vertebrates adapt to living on land?
    a. legs   **c.** watertight eggs
    b. lungs   **d.** all of the above

_____ **9.** When the dinosaurs first appeared, all of the continents were joined in a single supercontinent called
    a. North America.   **c.** South America.
    b. Pangaea.   **d.** Africa.

_____ **10.** One reason dinosaurs were so successful is that
    a. as predators, they eliminated many other species.
    b. they thrived in the mountainous environment.
    c. thecodonts and many other species became extinct.
    d. they were better suited for the cold climate.

_____ **11.** Animals whose body temperature changes as the temperature of their environment changes are called
    a. endotherms.   **c.** monotremes.
    b. thecodonts.   **d.** ectotherms.

_____ **12.** One way that crocodiles resemble birds more than they resemble other reptiles is their
    a. breastbone.   **c.** heart structure.
    b. brain size.   **d.** None of the above

_____ **13.** Ostracoderms
    a. were jawless fish.   **c.** evolved before placoderms.
    b. had primitive fins.   **d.** All of the above

Questions 14–16 refer to the figure below.

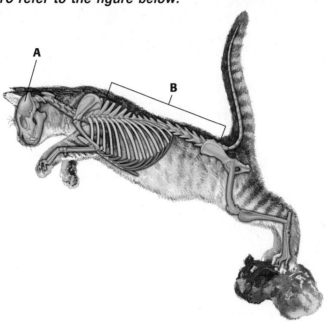

_____ 14. The kind of chordate shown in this diagram is a(n)

    a. tunicate.   **c.** vertebrate.

    b. echinoderm.   **d.** lancelet.

_____ 15. The individual segments that make up the structure labeled *B* are called

    a. scales.   **c.** bony plates.

    b. organs.   **d.** vertebrae.

_____ 16. An advantage to having the structure labeled *A* is that it

    a. provides support for the dorsal nerve cord.

    b. encases and protects the brain.

    c. protects the dorsal nerve cord.

    d. All of the above

Complete each statement by writing the correct term or phrase in the space provided.

17. Amphibians evolved a(n) _____ that delivers oxygen to the body more efficiently.

18. Dinosaurs were able to dominate amphibians when environmental conditions

    became _____ .

19. Traits shared by *Archaeopteryx* and modern birds include

    _____ and a fused _____ .

20. _____ are born prematurely and then complete development inside the mother's pouch.

Read each question, and write your answer in the space provided.

21. Explain how having jaws and paired fins was an advantage for early fishes.

_____

_____

_____

22. Describe one explanation for the extinction of the dinosaurs during the Cretaceous period.

_____

_____

_____

_____

23. Trace the events that led to mammals becoming the dominant animal group on land.

_____

_____

_____

24. Differentiate between cold-blooded and warm-blooded animals.

_____

_____

_____

_____

_____

25. Describe Earth's environmental conditions during the existence of Pangaea.

_____

_____

_____

Fishes and Amphibians

Circle T *if the statement is true or* F *if it is false.*

T   F   **1.** Some fish fertilize their eggs internally through spawning.

T   F   **2.** In fish, oxygen-rich blood passes from the gills to the heart and then to the rest of the body.

T   F   **3.** Marine fish need to make up for the water lost through osmosis.

T   F   **4.** In amphibians, the blood that is pumped from the heart to the body is completely oxygenated.

T   F   **5.** In amphibians, wastes exit the body through the cloacal opening.

In the space provided, write the letter of the term or phrase that best completes each statement or best answers each question.

_____ **6.** Gills, single-loop circulation, and a vertebral column are found in
     a. bony fishes.
     b. cartilaginous fishes.
     c. jawless fishes.
     d. All of the above

_____ **7.** Members of Osteichthyes
     a. have skeletons made of bone.
     b. do not have jaws.
     c. include rays and skates.
     d. All of the above

_____ **8.** The living agnathans are the
     a. lampreys and sharks.   **c.** hagfishes and coelacanths.
     b. sharks and rays.   **d.** lampreys and hagfishes.

_____ **9.** Cartilaginous fishes have all of the following EXCEPT
     a. an operculum.   **c.** a swim bladder.
     b. internal fertilization.   **d.** gill slits.

_____ **10.** Freshwater fish tend to take in water through osmosis and therefore excrete
     a. small amounts of concentrated urine.
     b. large amounts of concentrated urine.
     c. small amounts of diluted urine.
     d. large amounts of diluted urine.

_____ **11.** Members of the order Anura
     a. retain gills as adults.
     b. bear live young.
     c. undergo metamorphosis.
     d. have small, bony scales embedded in their skin.

_____ **12.** Fish absorb oxygen through their
  a. gill slits.
  b. swim bladder.
  c. gill filaments.
  d. mouth.

_____ **13.** A fish propels itself forward with its
  a. caudal fin.   **c.** pectoral fins.
  b. pelvic fins.   **d.** dorsal fins.

_____ **14.** In fish, undigested food exits the body through the
  a. cloaca.   **c.** intestine.
  b. anus.   **d.** ventral anal fin.

_____ **15.** The fish heart is an evolutionary advance for vertebrates because it pumps fully oxygenated blood
  a. through a double loop to the body's tissues.
  b. and has a divided ventricle.
  c. through a single loop to the body's tissues.
  d. and has a divided atrium.

_____ **16.** Bony fishes regulate their buoyancy with their
  a. pectoral fins.   **c.** gills.
  b. swim bladder.   **d.** lateral line.

Questions 17 and 18 refer to the figure at right, which shows the lateral line system.

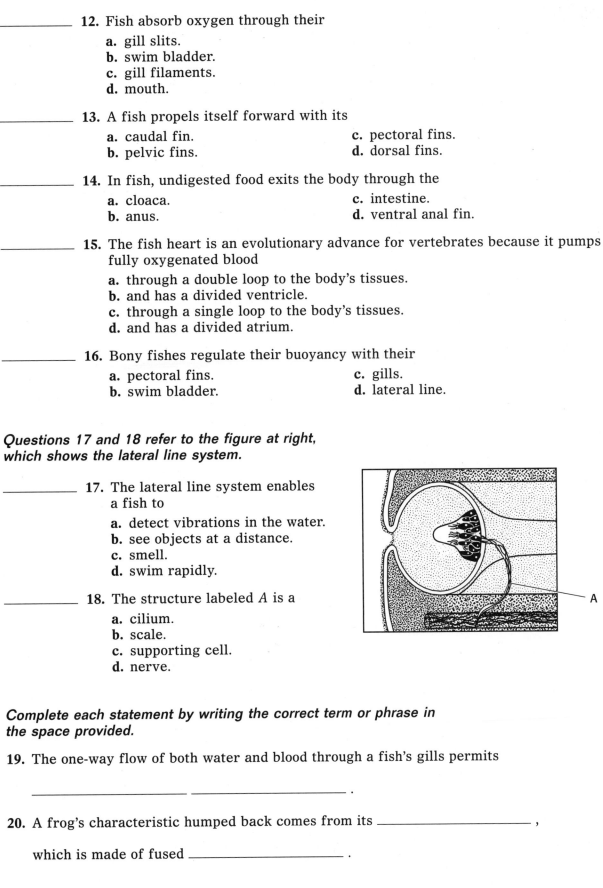

_____ **17.** The lateral line system enables a fish to
  a. detect vibrations in the water.
  b. see objects at a distance.
  c. smell.
  d. swim rapidly.

_____ **18.** The structure labeled *A* is a
  a. cilium.
  b. scale.
  c. supporting cell.
  d. nerve.

Complete each statement by writing the correct term or phrase in the space provided.

19. The one-way flow of both water and blood through a fish's gills permits

_____ _____ .

20. A frog's characteristic humped back comes from its _____ ,

which is made of fused _____ .

21. The changes that transform a tadpole into an adult frog are called

_____ .

22. In amphibians, the blood vessels that carry blood from the lungs to the heart

are called the _____ veins.

23. In frogs, the eardrum is called the _____ _____ .

Read each question, and write your answer in the space provided.

24. Trace the circulation of blood through the amphibian heart.

_____

_____

_____

_____

_____

_____

_____

_____

_____

25. Explain the importance of the operculum to bony fishes.

_____

_____

_____

_____

Reptiles and Birds

Circle T *if the statement is true or* F *if it is false.*

T   F   **1.** All reptiles have a partially divided ventricle.

T   F   **2.** An amniotic egg contains water and food for the embryo.

T   F   **3.** Air sacs connected to a bird's lungs permit one-way air flow.

T   F   **4.** A pit organ enables a rattlesnake to detect chemical odors.

In the space provided, write the letter of the term or phrase that best completes each statement or best answers each question.

_____   **5.** Crocodilians are distinguished by their
   a. air sacs.   **c.** partially divided ventricle.
   b. fully divided ventricle.   **d.** shelled egg.

_____   **6.** Which of the following is true of snakes?
   a. They have limbs.   **c.** They lack external ears.
   b. They have movable eyelids.   **d.** all of the above

_____   **7.** Only birds have
   a. feathers.   **c.** keeled breastbones.
   b. fused collarbones.   **d.** All of the above

_____   **8.** A bird's skeleton is
   a. composed of thin, hollow bones.
   b. more rigid than a reptile's skeleton.
   c. composed of many fused bones.
   d. All of the above

_____   **9.** A bird's crop
   a. temporarily stores food.
   b. is the first chamber of its stomach.
   c. is critical for flight.
   d. often contains small stones that the bird swallowed.

_____   **10.** In flying birds, large flight muscles are directly attached to
   a. leg muscles.   **c.** the keeled breastbone.
   b. feathers.   **d.** air sacs.

_____   **11.** Unlike other living reptiles, crocodilians
   a. care for their young after the young hatch.
   b. use internal fertilization.
   c. are oviparous.
   d. are ectothermic.

_____   **12.** The most important adaptations that helped reptiles succeed on land were
   a. lungs.   **c.** scales.
   b. watertight skin and eggs.   **d.** vertically positioned legs.

Questions 13–16 refer to the figure below, which shows the structure of a bird.

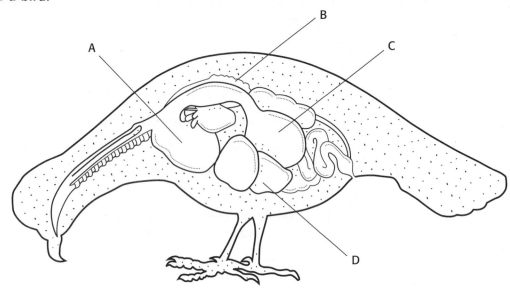

_____ **13.** The structure labeled *A* is the

    a. gizzard.   **c.** heart.

    b. liver.   **d.** crop.

_____ **14.** The structure labeled *C* is the

    a. gizzard.   **c.** heart.

    b. liver.   **d.** crop.

_____ **15.** The structure responsible for kneading and crushing food is labeled

    a. *A.*   **c.** *C.*

    b. *B.*   **d.** *D.*

_____ **16.** What characteristics are required for a beak used to tear apart prey or vegetation?

    a. long, spear-shaped   **c.** chisel-shaped

    b. hooked, curved, and pointed   **d.** thin, slightly curved

Complete each statement by writing the correct term or phrase in the space provided.

17. Reptiles, whose body temperature changes with the temperature of their

surroundings, are _____ .

18. The lower (ventral) portion of a tortoise's shell is called the

_____ .

19. Order Rynchocephalia includes only two living species of

_____ , which have survived nearly unchanged for 150 million years.

Name_____ Date _____ Class _____

20. Small chambers called _____ on the inner surface of a reptile's

lungs and strong _____ attached to the rib cage increase the
efficiency of the lungs.

21. Rattlesnakes inject venom into their prey through _____ .

22. _____ provide lift for flight, conserve _____

_____ , and sometimes provide protective

_____ .

23. In the ratio of _____ size to body size, _____
rank second among vertebrates.

Read each question, and write your answer in the space provided.

24. Name two types of feathers, and describe their functions.

_____

_____

_____

_____

_____

_____

25. What is a pit organ, and how does it benefit a rattlesnake?

_____

_____

_____

_____

_____

_____

_____

CHAPTER

(36) TEST

Mammals

Circle T *if the statement is true or* F *if it is false.*

T   F   **1.** Whales are examples of mammals that do not have hair.

T   F   **2.** The gestation period in marsupials is far shorter than the gestation period in placental mammals.

T   F   **3.** Most species of mammals are placental.

Questions 4 and 5 refer to the figures below, which show two mammalian skulls.

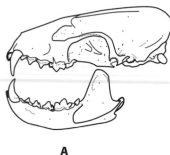   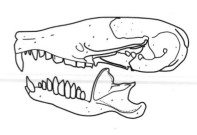

A   **B**

T   F   **4.** The skull labeled *A* is most likely that of a herbivore.

T   F   **5.** The skull labeled *B* has molars and canine teeth.

In the space provided, write the letter of the term or phrase that best completes each statement or best answers each question.

_____ **6.** All ungulates are able to digest cellulose with the help of
  a. rumens.   **c.** premolars.
  b. microbes.   **d.** flat molars.

_____ **7.** Members of the order Pinnipedia have
  a. streamlined bodies.   **c.** limbs modified into flippers.
  b. blowholes.   **d.** Both (a) and (c)

_____ **8.** Although a grizzly bear's metabolism slows in winter, the grizzly bear is still
  a. endothermic.   **c.** able to eat and drink.
  b. ectothermic.   **d.** Both (a) and (c)

_____ **9.** An animal that hatches from an egg, has fur, and obtains milk from its mother is a(n)
  a. placental mammal.   **c.** marsupial.
  b. monotreme.   **d.** insectivore.

_____ **10.** Dugongs and sea cows are
    a. toothless mammals.
    b. hoofed mammals.
    c. sirenians.
    d. marine hunters.

_____ **11.** Unlike reptiles, mammalian young depend on parental care for
    a. food.
    c. learning.
    b. protection.
    d. All of the above

_____ **12.** Antlers are
    a. made of bone and shed each year.
    b. permanently attached to the skull.
    c. made of keratin and shed each year.
    d. made of bone and keratin.

_____ **13.** If an animal has long canine teeth and sharp molars, it is probably a
    a. herbivore.
    b. carnivore.
    c. rodent.
    d. deer.

_____ **14.** In the development of cats, gorillas, and whales, nourishment and oxygen are provided by the mother to the fetus through the
    a. placenta.
    b. excretory system.
    c. uterus.
    d. Both (a) and (c)

_____ **15.** A mammal can use its teeth for
    a. chewing food.
    b. a threat signal.
    c. protection.
    d. All of the above

Complete each statement by writing the correct term or phrase in the space provided.

16. The only surviving monotremes are the _____

_____ and two species of _____ .

17. Instead of a(n) _____ , perissodactyls have a(n)

_____ branching off their large intestine that contains

_____ , which aid(s) in the digestion of cellulose.

18. Members of the orders Cetacea and Sirenia have flattened

_____ for _____ through the water.

19. An animal that maintains a high, nearly constant body temperature through

metabolism is said to be _____ .

20. The period of time between fertilization and birth in placentals and marsupials

is called the _____ .

21. Newborn marsupials complete their development in the mother's

_____ .

22. Rodents have been successful because of their _____ , small

size, and rapid rate of _____ .

23. _____ , mammals with an even number of toes, include pigs, hippopotamuses, camels, deer, and antelope.

Read each question, and write your answer in the space provided.

24. What are the functions of hair on a mammal?

_____

_____

_____

_____

_____

25. Why do scientists think that monotremes are more closely related to early mammals than are any other living mammals?

_____

_____

_____

_____

_____

CHAPTER
37 **TEST**

Animal Behavior

Circle T *if the statement is true or* F *if it is false.*

T F **1.** Innate behaviors are genetically programmed.

T F **2.** Locating food is an example of territorial behavior.

T F **3.** New male lions in a pride kill cubs of other males because they know it will benefit them as individuals.

T F **4.** Visual signals are only efficient when the sender and the receiver are near each other.

In the space provided, write the letter of the term or phrase that best completes each statement or best answers each question.

_____ **5.** An evolutionary mechanism in which traits that increase an individual's ability to attract a mate appear with increased frequency is
  a. a fixed action pattern.
  b. behavioral selection.
  c. sexual selection.
  d. natural selection.

_____ **6.** The ability to perform a behavior is often innate, but the final shape of the genetically programmed behavior is often the result of
  a. learning.
  b. habituation.
  c. operant conditioning.
  d. imprinting.

_____ **7.** A scientist asks a "why" question about a behavior to understand the
  a. reasons it exists.
  b. evolution of the behavior.
  c. reasons it continues today.
  d. All of the above

_____ **8.** Animals usually behave in ways that are favorable for them because natural selection favors traits that
  a. benefit the species.
  b. benefit the individual.
  c. benefit behavior.
  d. are innate.

_____ **9.** Extreme traits—such as antlers, increased size, and lion manes—that are found in male animals but not females are the result of
  a. evolution.
  b. sexual selection.
  c. natural selection.
  d. All of the above

Question 10 refers to the figure at right.

_____ 10. In the figure at right, the bird providing food to its young is engaging in

    a. foraging behavior.
    b. parental care.
    c. imprinting.
    d. territorial behavior.

_____ 11. Which of the following involves learning?

    a. reasoning   **c.** trial-and-error
    b. classical conditioning   **d.** all of the above

_____ 12. In Pavlov's experiment, meat powder caused the dogs to salivate; this is an example of

    a. classical conditioning.   **c.** trial-and-error.
    b. innate behavior.   **d.** reasoning.

_____ 13. When imprinting, young birds will follow

    a. their mother.
    b. only members of other species.
    c. the first moving object they see.
    d. only members of their species.

_____ 14. Which of the following is NOT a use for a signal?

    a. attracting a mate   **c.** finding food
    b. showing submission   **d.** warning of danger

Complete each statement by writing the correct term or phrase in the space provided.

15. The ability to analyze a problem and use past experience to develop

insight is called _____ .

16. When a male animal establishes boundaries during mating season and will not

let another male go near the females, he is engaging in _____

_____ .

17. An understanding of _____ _____ can help
answer a "why" behavioral question.

18. The development of behaviors through experience is called

_____ .

19. Birds that ignore a scarecrow in the garden every day are demonstrating

_____ .

20. Most biologists think that behavior has both _____ and

_____ components.

21. One _____ behavior in spiders is web building, which is also a(n)

_____ _____ _____

behavior.

22. In humans, the ability to learn language rapidly seems to be

_____ _____ , but the production of the

sounds while learning to speak occurs by trial-and-error, which is a(n)

_____ behavior.

Read each question, and write your answer in the space provided.

23. Why is it important that courtship signals be unique for each species?

_____

_____

_____

24. How does natural selection explain why male lions new to a pride kill the cubs
of other males?

_____

_____

_____

_____

_____

25. Recall that a rat in a "Skinner box" and a chimpanzee in a room each obtained
food that was hidden or placed out of reach. Explain why the rat demonstrated
operant conditioning and the chimp demonstrated reasoning.

_____

_____

_____

_____

_____

Introduction to Body Structure

Circle T *if the statement is true or* F *if it is false.*

T   F   **1.** Haversian canals contain bone marrow.

T   F   **2.** The chances of developing osteoporosis can be reduced by a mineral-rich diet and regular exercise.

T   F   **3.** Ligaments cushion the ends of the bones of a joint.

T   F   **4.** Resistance exercises, such as pull-ups, are mostly aerobic.

In the space provided, write the letter of the term or phrase that best completes each statement or best answers each question.

_____   **5.** Smooth muscle is also called
     a. rhythmic muscle.   **c.** interconnected muscle.
     b. voluntary muscle.   **d.** involuntary muscle.

_____   **6.** Which of the following is NOT part of the immune system?
     a. heart   **c.** skin
     b. lymph nodes   **d.** white blood cells

_____   **7.** Which of the following is NOT a hinge joint?
     a. elbow   **c.** finger knuckle
     b. wrist   **d.** toe knuckle

_____   **8.** Osteoporosis is a medical condition that results from
     a. too much dietary calcium.
     b. failure to convert cartilage to bone during development.
     c. an excessive rate of bone replacement.
     d. inefficient bone replacement later in life.

_____   **9.** The origin of a muscle
     a. is at the opposite end of the muscle from the insertion.
     b. is the bone that remains stationary when the muscle contracts.
     c. does not move when the muscle contracts.
     d. All of the above

_____   **10.** The total amount of force that a muscle contraction can exert
     a. is not influenced by nerve impulses.
     b. depends on the total number of muscle fibers that are contracted.
     c. depends on the weight of the object being moved.
     d. is the same for all muscles.

_____   **11.** Aerobic exercises are beneficial because they
     a. increase muscle size and strength.
     b. result in more-efficient ATP production.
     c. use up glycogen stores quickly.
     d. prevent myosin and actin linkages in muscles.

_____ **12.** The dermis is
   a. composed of hair and nails.
   b. the outermost layer of the skin.
   c. mostly dead cells.
   d. involved in temperature regulation.

_____ **13.** Hair and nails are derived from cells of the
   a. dermis.
   b. subcutaneous tissue.
   c. oil glands.
   d. epidermis.

Questions 14–16 refer to the figure below, which shows three different joints.

A   B   C

_____ **14.** Which of the joints shown above is a ball-and-socket joint?
   a. *A*
   b. *B*
   c. *C*
   d. none of the above

_____ **15.** Joint *B* is most likely an illustration of a
   a. ball-and-socket joint.
   b. hinge joint.
   c. gliding joint.
   d. saddle joint.

_____ **16.** Gliding motion occurs in the joint labeled
   a. *A*.
   b. *B*.
   c. *C*.
   d. None of the above

Complete each statement by writing the correct term or phrase in the space provided.

17. The _____ is a tough membrane that surrounds bones.

18. The rib cage is formed by curved ribs extending from the backbone, joining together in the front at a bone called the _____ .

19. A large fluid-filled space that houses and protects major internal organs is called a(n) _____ .

20. Muscles that cause a joint to straighten are called _____ .

Read each question, and write your answer in the space provided.

21. Briefly describe the interaction of muscle filaments during a muscle contraction.

_____

_____

_____

_____

22. What is the outermost layer of the skin, and what is its function?

_____

_____

_____

_____

23. Describe how bone cells are nourished and maintained.

_____

_____

_____

_____

24. Describe the process of bone formation from early development through middle age.

_____

_____

_____

_____

25. Briefly describe the causes of acne and skin cancer. What can be done to prevent these skin disorders?

_____

_____

_____

_____

CHAPTER
39 **TEST**

Circulatory and Respiratory Systems

Circle T *if the statement is true or* F *if it is false.*

T   F   **1.** One of the main functions of the human circulatory system is to distribute nutrients and other molecules to all parts of the body.

T   F   **2.** When a platelet encounters a damaged blood vessel, it releases fibrin, which causes a clot to form.

T   F   **3.** The diameter of arteries is smaller than the diameter of veins.

T   F   **4.** Swollen lymph nodes may indicate an infection.

In the space provided, write the letter of the term or phrase that best completes each statement or best answers each question.

_____ **5.** Excess fluids and proteins in the body are returned to the bloodstream by
    a. the heart.   **c.** the respiratory system.
    b. arteries.   **d.** the lymphatic system.

_____ **6.** If a blood vessel has valves, it probably
    a. is a vein.   **c.** is a capillary.
    b. is an artery.   **d.** is mutated.

_____ **7.** A person with type B blood can receive type
    a. AB blood.   **c.** O or B blood.
    b. AB or B blood.   **d.** A blood.

_____ **8.** The pulmonary circulation loop carries blood to the
    a. kidneys.   **c.** intestines.
    b. liver.   **d.** lungs.

_____ **9.** A respiratory disease in which airways in the lungs become narrow because of sensitivity to certain stimuli is called
    a. asthma.   **c.** emphysema.
    b. lung cancer.   **d.** alveolar reduction.

_____ **10.** The respiratory control center in the brain is most sensitive to the concentration of
    a. oxygen.
    b. carbon dioxide in the lungs.
    c. carbon dioxide in the blood.
    d. carbon dioxide in the cells.

_____ **11.** The tiny electrical impulses produced by the heart muscle when it contracts can be monitored using a(n)
    a. stethoscope.
    b. sphygmomanometer.
    c. electrocardiograph.
    d. watch.

Name_____ Date _____ Class_____

Questions 12–15 refer to the figure at right, which shows the human heart.

_____ **12.** Blood in the chamber labeled *C*
   a. is full of oxygen.
   b. is returning from the lungs.
   c. is oxygen-poor.
   d. has very little plasma.

_____ **13.** The vessel labeled *E*, which carries deoxygenated blood, is
   a. a pulmonary artery.
   b. a pulmonary vein.
   c. part of the aorta.
   d. part of the atria.

_____ **14.** The chamber labeled *F* is the
   a. right atrium.
   b. left atrium.
   c. right ventricle.
   d. left ventricle.

_____ **15.** The chamber labeled *G* pumps blood into the structure labeled
   a. *A*.   **c.** *E*.
   b. *B*.   **d.** *G*.

Complete each statement by writing the correct term or phrase in the space provided.

16. The contractions of the heart, initiated by the sinoatrial node, cause the right

and left _____ to contract first.

17. The danger of having high blood pressure, or _____ , is that if it is left untreated, it can lead to heart damage, brain damage, or kidney failure.

18. The oxygen-carrying molecule in red blood cells is called

_____ .

19. Breathing occurs because of differences between the _____

_____ inside the lungs and outside the body.

Read each question, and write your answer in the space provided.

20. Describe how white blood cells help the body fight disease.

_____

_____

_____

21. Summarize how carbon dioxide is transported in the blood.

_____

_____

_____

_____

22. Summarize the path that air follows when it enters the body.

_____

_____

_____

_____

23. Relate the structure of arteries and capillaries to their function.

_____

_____

_____

_____

24. List five types of molecules transported by the circulatory system.

_____

_____

_____

_____

25. Identify four components found in plasma.

_____

_____

_____

_____

Digestive and Excretory Systems

Circle T *if the statement is true or* F *if it is false.*

T   F   **1.** Excess calories that a person consumes are metabolized to produce heat energy.

T   F   **2.** Calcium is an example of a mineral that the body requires.

T   F   **3.** The rectum is the final section of the digestive tract.

T   F   **4.** Urea is a highly toxic, nitrogenous waste.

In the space provided, write the letter of the term or phrase that best completes each statement or best answers each question.

_____   **5.** Vitamins are compounds that
   a. enhance the activities of enzymes.
   b. provide energy.
   c. form cell membranes.
   d. are enzymes.

_____   **6.** The wavelike contractions of smooth muscle that move food down the esophagus are called
   a. peristaltic contractions.
   b. voluntary contractions.
   c. peristaltic reflexes.
   d. involuntary contractions.

_____   **7.** Food passes from the stomach into the
   a. colon.
   b. esophagus.
   c. small intestine.
   d. liver.

_____   **8.** Bile
   a. breaks globules of fat into tiny droplets.
   b. is stored in the gallbladder.
   c. is produced by the liver.
   d. All of the above

_____   **9.** Too much bile pigment in the blood can result in
   a. the breakdown of hemoglobin.   **c.** jaundice.
   b. cirrhosis.   **d.** hepatitis.

_____   **10.** A kidney dialysis machine
   a. reduces blood volume.
   b. increases blood volume.
   c. removes wastes from the blood.
   d. oxygenates the patient's blood.

Name_____ Date _____ Class _____

Questions 11–13 refer to the figure at right.

_____ **11.** The structure labeled *B* is a
  a. villus.
  b. nephron.
  c. ureter.
  d. urethra.

_____ **12.** Structure *B* is found in the
  a. kidneys.
  b. esophagus.
  c. small intestine.
  d. tongue.

_____ **13.** Structure *B* allows for an increase in
  a. absorption area.
  b. mechanical digestion.
  c. acid production.
  d. bile production.

_____ **14.** From the villi, fatty acids and glycerol will enter the
  a. large intestine.   **c.** capillaries.
  b. lymphatic vessels.   **d.** Both (b) and (c)

_____ **15.** Which of the following is NOT a nutrient?
  a. lipids   **c.** water
  b. carbohydrates   **d.** proteins

_____ **16.** Damaged kidneys will affect the body's ability to rid itself of
  a. excess water.
  b. excess salt.
  c. toxic chemicals.
  d. All of the above

Complete each statement by writing the correct term or phrase in the space provided.

17. To help prevent heart disease, you should consume no more than 30 percent of your calories from _____ each day.

18. The eight amino acids that humans are unable to manufacture are called _____ amino acids.

19. Digestion is the process of breaking down _____ into _____ the body can use.

20. The _____ secretes digestive enzymes that help complete the digestion of carbohydrates, proteins, and lipids.

21. _____ aids in human digestion by stimulating the walls of the digestive tract to secrete mucus.

Biology: Principles and Explorations **Test** Chapter 40 **119**

Read each question, and write your answer in the space provided.

22. The structure of proteins makes it difficult for the body to digest them. How does the body solve the problem of digesting proteins?

_____

_____

_____

_____

_____

23. Summarize how the body excretes waste products.

_____

_____

_____

_____

24. Summarize the recommendations of the USDA's food pyramid in order of the daily number of servings recommended from each food group.

_____

_____

_____

_____

25. Explain why females are more prone to urinary infections than are males.

_____

_____

_____

_____

_____

CHAPTER
41 **TEST**

The Body's Defenses

Circle T *if the statement is true or* F *if it is false.*

T   F   **1.** Natural killer cells attack infected cells but not the pathogens that caused the infection.

T   F   **2.** Cytotoxic T cells and B cells are activated by interleukin-2, which is secreted by helper T cells.

T   F   **3.** Every person who is HIV positive has the disease called AIDS.

In the space provided, write the letter of the term or phrase that best completes each statement or best answers each question.

_____ **4.** Mucus is produced by cells lining the walls of the bronchi and bronchioles
     a. only when a person has a severe respiratory infection.
     b. to allow oxygen to diffuse into the blood more efficiently.
     c. as a lubricant for the expulsion of food that might "go down the wrong tube."
     d. to protect against pathogens that might be inhaled.

_____ **5.** The stomach is involved in defense against infection because it
     a. regurgitates any pathogen that might be swallowed.
     b. secretes mucus, which is carried away by cilia.
     c. contains acid that destroys pathogens that are swallowed.
     d. sends potential pathogens to the liver for destruction.

_____ **6.** White blood cells that carry out nonspecific defenses include
     a. macrophages.   **c.** natural killer cells.
     b. neutrophils.   **d.** All of the above

_____ **7.** Pus associated with some infections consists of
     a. dead or dying white blood cells.
     b. broken-down tissue cells.
     c. dead pathogens.
     d. All of the above

_____ **8.** Which of the following pairs is NOT correctly associated?
     a. cytotoxic T cells—attack and kill infected cells
     b. helper T cells—activate cytotoxic T cells and B cells
     c. B cells—engulf cells that are infected with pathogens
     d. macrophages—consume pathogens and infected cells

_____ **9.** Some of the B cells that have encountered a pathogen
     a. become cytotoxic T cells.
     b. are ingested by macrophages.
     c. have viral proteins on their cell membrane.
     d. become memory cells.

_____ **10.** Vaccines are effective in preventing disease because they
    a. trigger an immune response without causing disease.
    b. contain antibodies directed against specific pathogens.
    c. contain specific B cells and T cells.
    d. contain pathogens to which the person is already immune.

_____ **11.** Immunization against an influenza virus does not provide long-term protection against the disease because
    a. the virus mutates and produces new antigens.
    b. antibodies do not work against viruses.
    c. the vaccine used to immunize people against influenza causes the virus to change.
    d. the virus destroys the vaccine before it has a chance to work.

_____ **12.** HIV causes AIDS by attacking and destroying
    a. helper T cells.   **c.** neutrophils.
    b. B cells.   **d.** antibodies.

_____ **13.** Skin and mucous membranes
    a. are nonspecific defenses.
    b. provide physical barriers to pathogens.
    c. produce chemicals to eliminate pathogens.
    d. All of the above

_____ **14.** The release of histamine is part of the
    a. temperature response.
    b. first line of nonspecific defenses.
    c. inflammatory response.
    d. Both (b) and (c)

Complete each statement by writing the correct term or phrase in the space provided.

15. _____ T cells kill infected cells, and B cells identify _____ for destruction by macrophages.

16. _____ are white blood cells that travel throughout the body, killing pathogens by ingesting them.

17. Interleukin-2 is produced by _____ T cells.

18. After activation by interleukin-2, B cells develop into _____ and produce _____ .

19. _____ is a chemical that is released during an allergic reaction.

20. A condition in which the immune system cannot distinguish between pathogens and the body's own cells is called a(n) _____ disease.

21. _____ is a protein released by cells infected with viruses.

Name_____ Date _____ Class_____

Read each question, and write your answer in the space provided.

22. Briefly describe how a cell that has been infected by a virus can be recognized and destroyed by the body.

_____

_____

_____

_____

_____

_____

23. List five ways diseases can be directly transmitted to humans.

_____

_____

24. How is the human immunodeficiency virus (HIV) transmitted, and how does it disable the immune system?

_____

_____

_____

_____

Question 25 refers to the graph at right.

25. Which period of time would involve the most rapid division of B cells? Explain.

_____

_____

_____

_____

_____

_____

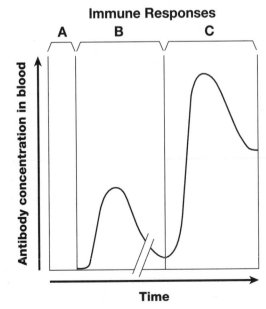

Immune Responses

A   B   C

Antibody concentration in blood

Time

Name_____ Date _____ Class _____

Nervous System

Circle T *if the statement is true or* F *if it is false.*

T F **1.** Memory, learning, and emotions are controlled by the autonomic nervous system.

T F **2.** Thermoreceptors are located in the skin and hypothalamus.

T F **3.** Addiction to psychoactive drugs is a physiological response because repeated use of a psychoactive drug alters the normal functioning of neurons and synapses.

T F **4.** Alcoholism can lead to malnutrition, liver damage, and inflammation of the stomach lining.

In the space provided, write the letter of the term or phrase that best completes each statement or best answers each question.

_____ **5.** The myelin sheath
  a. transmits impulses.   **c.** insulates axons.
  b. insulates synapses.   **d.** None of the above

_____ **6.** The two principal components of the peripheral nervous system are the
  a. somatic and the autonomic nervous systems.
  b. sensory and motor divisions.
  c. autonomic and central nervous systems.
  d. sympathetic and the parasympathetic divisions.

_____ **7.** The dorsal roots of spinal nerves contain
  a. sensory neurons.   **c.** interneurons.
  b. dendrites.   **d.** motor neurons.

_____ **8.** Nicotine mimics the action of the neurotransmitter
  a. dopamine.   **c.** glutamate.
  b. acetylcholine.   **d.** None of the above

_____ **9.** Narcotics
  a. are extremely addictive.
  b. mimic natural painkillers called enkephalins.
  c. affect the limbic system, producing a feeling of well-being.
  d. All of the above

_____ **10.** Nitrous oxide, ether, paint thinner, and glue belong to a class of psychoactive drugs called
  a. stimulants.   **c.** depressants.
  b. inhalants.   **d.** hallucinogens.

_____ **11.** When a neuron is at rest,
  a. sodium ions are more concentrated outside the cell.
  b. potassium ions are more concentrated inside the cell.
  c. the inside of the cell is negatively charged.
  d. All of the above

Name _____ Date _____ Class _____

Questions 12 and 13 refer to the figure below.

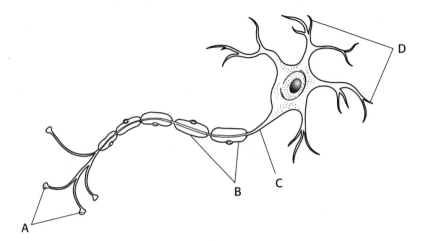

_____ **12.** The structures labeled *D* are called
  a. dendrites.   **c.** nodes.
  b. axons.   **d.** axon terminals.

_____ **13.** An action potential is conducted down the axon, which is labeled
  a. *A.*   **c.** *C.*
  b. *B.*   **d.** *D.*

_____ **14.** During a nerve impulse,
  a. sodium ions first rush out of the cell.
  b. there is a reversal of polarity in the axon.
  c. the membrane potential of the cell does not change.
  d. potassium ions are pumped into the axon.

Complete each statement by writing the correct term or phrase in the space provided.

15. Extensions from the cell body of a neuron called _____ receive information from other neurons.

16. A(n) _____ is an involuntary, self-protective motor response.

17. A synaptic cleft is the gap between a(n) _____ neuron and a(n)

_____ cell.

18. _____ are sensory receptors that respond to physical stimuli that cause distortion or bending of tissue.

19. _____ receptors are chemoreceptors located in the roof of the nasal passage.

20. Sensory information about hearing is processed in the _____ lobe of the brain.

Read each question, and write your answer in the space provided.

21. How is a signal from a presynaptic neuron transmitted to a postsynaptic cell?

_____

_____

_____

_____

22. Describe the function of the cerebrum.

_____

_____

_____

_____

23. Distinguish between addiction and tolerance.

_____

_____

_____

_____

24. Describe how the ear converts sound waves into electrical impulses that the brain can process.

_____

_____

_____

25. Describe the action of cocaine at a synapse.

_____

_____

_____

_____

Hormones and the Endocrine System

Circle T *if the statement is true or* F *if it is false.*

T   F   **1.** Prostaglandins are secreted only by the brain.

T   F   **2.** Feedback mechanisms for hormones work by detecting the amount of hormones already in circulation or the amount of other chemicals produced because of hormone action.

T   F   **3.** A steroid hormone-receptor complex can bind to DNA and either activate or inhibit gene expression.

T   F   **4.** The hypothalamus and the pituitary gland control the initial release of many hormones.

In the space provided, write the letter of the term or phrase that best completes each statement or best answers each question.

_____ **5.** The instructions hormones carry are determined by
   a. the hormone.
   b. both the hormone itself and the cell it binds.
   c. the target cell.
   d. the messenger cell.

_____ **6.** All of the following are hormonelike substances EXCEPT
   a. sweat.   **c.** prostaglandins.
   b. enkephalins.   **d.** endorphins.

_____ **7.** Compared with a neurotransmitter, the life span of a hormone is
   a. shorter.   **c.** unpredictable.
   b. the same.   **d.** longer.

_____ **8.** Which of the following are endocrine glands?
   a. pancreas
   b. testes
   c. pituitary gland
   d. all of the above

_____ **9.** When an amino-acid-based hormone attaches to a receptor protein,
   a. the hormone-receptor complex then binds to DNA.
   b. the hormone passes through the cell membrane.
   c. the shape of the receptor protein changes.
   d. the hormone is converted to a steroid.

_____ **10.** Thyroid hormones
   a. regulate the body's metabolic rate.
   b. promote normal growth of the brain, bones, and muscles during childhood.
   c. affect reproductive functions.
   d. All of the above

Name_____ Date _____ Class_____

Questions 11–15 refer to the figure at right, which shows the glands of the human endocrine system.

_____ 11. The pituitary gland is labeled
- **a.** *A.*
- **b.** *B.*
- **c.** *C.*
- **d.** *D.*

_____ 12. Development of secondary sex characteristics and gamete formation in females are stimulated by secretions of the gland labeled
- **a.** *C.*
- **b.** *D.*
- **c.** *E.*
- **d.** *F.*

_____ 13. The gland that produces the hormones insulin and glucagon is labeled
- **a.** *A.*
- **b.** *B.*
- **c.** *C.*
- **d.** *D.*

_____ 14. The gland that is stimulated during emergency situations, causing the fight-or-flight response, is labeled
- **a.** *A.*   **c.** *C.*
- **b.** *B.*   **d.** *E.*

_____ 15. Thyroid-stimulating hormone is secreted by the gland labeled
- **a.** *A.*   **c.** *C.*
- **b.** *B.*   **d.** *D.*

Complete each statement by writing the correct term or phrase in the space provided.

16. After hormones are released, they bind and act only on specific

_____ _____ .

17. The change in shape that occurs when a(n) _____

_____ _____ hormone binds to a receptor protein results in the activation of a second messenger.

18. The _____ controls many body functions by issuing instructions to the pituitary gland.

19. _____ hormones can pass through target cell membranes.

20. _____ is secreted by the posterior pituitary, and it triggers milk ejection during nursing and uterine contractions for childbirth.

Name_____ Date _____ Class _____

Read each question, and write your answer in the space provided.

21. Discuss the similarities and differences of the endocrine and nervous systems.

_____

_____

_____

_____

_____

_____

22. List four functions of hormones.

_____

_____

_____

23. Compare type I with type II diabetes.

_____

_____

_____

_____

_____

_____

24. What are the fight-or-flight hormones, and what are their effects on the body?

_____

_____

_____

25. Differentiate between endocrine and exocrine glands.

_____

_____

_____

CHAPTER
44 **TEST**

Reproduction and Development

Circle T *if the statement is true or* F *if it is false.*

T   F   **1.** In humans, both the male and female gamete-producing organs are located within the abdominal cavity.

T   F   **2.** Fertilization usually takes place in the fallopian tubes.

T   F   **3.** In its early stage, genital herpes can be cured using antibiotics.

T   F   **4.** The testes begin to produce sperm during the adolescent stage of puberty.

In the space provided, write the letter of the term or phrase that best completes each statement or best answers each question.

_____ **5.** The testes
 a. produce sperm.   c. are located in the scrotum.
 b. secrete testosterone.   d. All of the above

_____ **6.** As sperm move through the urethra, they mix with fluid secreted by the
 a. seminal vesicles.   c. bulbourethral glands.
 b. prostate gland.   d. All of the above

_____ **7.** The fallopian tubes
 a. secrete estrogen.
 b. produce eggs.
 c. are passageways through which an ovum travels.
 d. All of the above

_____ **8.** Menopause is the time at which
 a. the ovarian cycle begins.   c. the menstrual cycle begins.
 b. eggs are produced.   d. menstruation stops.

_____ **9.** In an embryo, major internal organs are evident
 a. during the sixth month.
 b. by the end of the third trimester.
 c. during the second month.
 d. just before birth.

_____ **10.** Sexually transmitted diseases caused by bacteria, such as gonorrhea and chlamydia,
 a. are almost always incurable.
 b. are not communicable.
 c. can be treated using antibiotics.
 d. None of the above

_____ **11.** A leading cause of birth defects is
 a. alcohol and drug use by pregnant women.
 b. exercise during pregnancy.
 c. poor diet during the second trimester of pregnancy.
 d. improper implantation.

_____ **12.** Luteinizing hormone and follicle-stimulating hormone are involved in
  a. sperm production.   **c.** implantation.
  b. the ovarian cycle.   **d.** Both (a) and (b)

_____ **13.** Eggs do not mature until
  a. the production of sex hormones increases.
  b. meiosis resumes.
  c. a female reaches puberty.
  d. All of the above

_____ **14.** Which of the following is NOT an STD?
  a. hepatitis B   **c.** chancre
  b. genital warts   **d.** chlamydia

_____ **15.** When sperm exit the body, they pass through the
  a. epididymis, vas deferens, and then the urethra.
  b. vas deferens, epididymis, and then the urethra.
  c. seminal vesicles, vas deferens, and then the urethra.
  d. vas deferens, seminiferous tubules, and then the urethra.

Complete each statement by writing the correct term or phrase in the space provided.

16. Because they are formed by _____ , sperm cells contain only 23 chromosomes instead of the usual diploid number found in body cells.

17. In males, the _____ _____ secretes a fluid that neutralizes the acids produced by the female reproductive system.

18. During the luteal phase, the corpus luteum secretes the hormone

_____ , which signals the body to prepare for fertilization.

19. When fertilization occurs, a(n) _____ is produced.

20. The blastocyst burrows into the lining of the uterus in an event called

_____ .

Read each question, and write your answer in the space provided.

21. Describe the structures of a sperm cell, and describe their roles in cell function.

_____

_____

_____

_____

_____

22. Describe the development that occurs in a fetus from the end of the first trimester to the end of the third trimester.

_____

_____

_____

_____

23. Explain how hormone levels regulate the menstrual cycle.

_____

_____

_____

_____

_____

Questions 24 and 25 refer to the figure below.

24. What event is illustrated by this figure? Identify the structures labeled *A–D*.

_____

_____

25. Blood levels of three hormones rise sharply before this event occurs. What are these hormones?

_____

_____

Answer Key

CHAPTER 1
Biology and You

TRUE/FALSE

1. T
2. F
3. F
4. T
5. T

MULTIPLE CHOICE

6. c
7. a
8. b
9. b
10. c
11. c
12. b
13. a
14. d
15. b

COMPLETION

16. cell
17. Heredity
18. energy
19. homeostasis
20. reproduction
21. DNA
22. gene therapy
23. cancer

ESSAY

24. *Hypothesis 1:* Excessive amounts of ultraviolet (UV) radiation can harm or kill amphibian eggs. *Hypothesis 2:* Excessive amounts of UV radiation can make adult amphibians ill or cause them to die. *Prediction:* Exposing amphibian eggs and adult amphibians to high levels of UV radiation will harm or kill amphibian eggs or adult amphibians. *Experiment:* Expose a control group of frog eggs or adult amphibians to low UV radiation levels. Expose the experimental group to high UV radiation levels. Both groups should be exposed for the same period of time. Both groups of eggs should be in water that is the same temperature and has a neutral pH. Knowledge of past and current UV radiation levels from several locations will aid in determining what qualifies as low, or normal, UV radiation levels and what is abnormally high.

25. No, the experiment was not a waste of time. A scientist works by methodically showing that hypotheses are either consistent or inconsistent with the results of experiments. The results of experiments are used to evaluate alternative hypotheses. An experiment can be successful if it shows that one or more of the alternative hypotheses are inconsistent with observations.

CHAPTER 2
Chemistry of Life

TRUE/FALSE

1. F
2. F
3. F
4. T
5. T

MULTIPLE CHOICE

6. d
7. b
8. a
9. b
10. c
11. d
12. d

COMPLETION

13. reactant, products
14. ionic
15. polar, nonpolar
16. molecules
17. acidic
18. substrates, active site
19. ATP
20. monosaccharides, energy
21. homeostasis

ESSAY

22. A—enzyme; B—substrate
23. An enzyme increases the speed of a chemical reaction by reducing the activation energy of the reaction.
24. Proteins are chains of amino acids, which can be polar or nonpolar. Proteins tend to fold into compact shapes. Nucleic acids are long chains of nucleotides. The two nucleic acids, DNA and RNA, each contain only four types of nucleotides. A nucleotide is composed of a sugar, a base, and a phosphate group. DNA has two chains, or strands, of nucleotides, and RNA has only one.
25. Covalent bonds link the hydrogen and oxygen atoms in each water molecule. Hydrogen bonds link the hydrogen and oxygen atoms of adjacent water molecules.

CHAPTER 3
Cell Structure

TRUE/FALSE

1. T
2. F
3. T
4. T
5. T

MULTIPLE CHOICE

6. b
7. c
8. b
9. d
10. a
11. d
12. c
13. b
14. c
15. a
16. d

COMPLETION

17. cell theory
18. nonpolar
19. Cilia, flagella
20. cytoskeleton
21. ocular, objective
22. rough

ESSAY

23. Mitochondria harvest energy from organic compounds to make ATP.
24. Magnification is a measure of the increase in the size of an image over the actual size of the object being examined. Resolution is a measure of the ability to clearly see an object being viewed. Magnification is only valuable as long as resolution is good.
25. (1) Marker proteins enable other cells to recognize a cell's identity. (2) Receptor proteins recognize and bind to specific substances outside the cell. (3) Enzymes are involved in biochemical reactions in the cell. (4) Transport proteins aid the movement of substances into and out of a cell.

CHAPTER 4

Cells and Their Environment

TRUE/FALSE

1. T
2. F
3. T
4. T

MULTIPLE CHOICE

5. b
6. c
7. d
8. b
9. c
10. b
11. a
12. b
13. c
14. d

COMPLETION

15. selectively
16. active transport
17. carrier proteins
18. endocytosis
19. receptor protein
20. hypertonic

ESSAY

21. Drinking sea water increases the concentration of salts in body fluids. This causes water to leave cells by osmosis.
22. Using energy from ATP, the sodium-potassium pump transports three sodium ions out of the cell. The pump then picks up two potassium ions from outside the cell and transports them into the cell. The ions move against their concentration gradient. The process is important because it prevents a buildup of sodium in the cell, which can be toxic, and because it helps maintain the concentration gradients of sodium and potassium ions across the cell membrane.
23. (1) The receptor protein can act as an enzyme or can activate enzymes inside the cell, chemically changing the molecules in the cytoplasm. (2) The receptor protein may cause the formation of a second messenger that can change the functioning of the cell by activating enzymes or opening ion channels, for example. (3) The receptor protein can open a channel through the membrane.
24. Diffusion is the random movement of a substance down its concentration gradient. Active transport is the movement of particles against their concentration gradient.
25. The rigid cell walls of plant and fungal cells prevent them from expanding too much. Some unicellular eukaryotes have contractile vacuoles that collect excess water and force it out of the cell. Many animal cells increase the water concentration inside the cell by removing dissolved particles from the cytoplasm.

CHAPTER 5

Photosynthesis and Cellular Respiration

TRUE/FALSE

1. T
2. F
3. T
4. F

MULTIPLE CHOICE

5. b
6. d
7. a
8. c
9. b
10. d
11. a
12. c
13. d
14. c
15. d

COMPLETION

16. sun
17. cellular respiration
18. Calvin cycle
19. NAD$^+$

20. Oxygen
21. Autotrophs
22. Photosynthesis
23. electrons

ESSAY

24. The energy used in the Calvin cycle is supplied by the ATP and NADPH that are produced in the first stage of photosynthesis.

25. In cells deprived of sufficient oxygen for aerobic respiration, pyruvate will undergo fermentation to recycle NAD^+. This recycled NAD^+ is needed to continue making ATP through glycolysis.

CHAPTER 6
Chromosomes and Cell Reproduction

TRUE/FALSE

1. T
2. F
3. F
4. F
5. T

MULTIPLE CHOICE

6. c
7. d
8. d
9. c
10. a
11. b
12. c
13. b

COMPLETION

14. zygote
15. Binary fission
16. interphase
17. gametes
18. spindle
19. genes, proteins
20. Homologous chromosomes
21. genes, chromosomes
22. deletion mutation

ESSAY

23. A karyotype is a photograph that shows the collection of chromosomes found in an individual's cells. Analysis of this collection of chromosomes can reveal abnormalities in chromosome number and structure. Down syndrome is associated with trisomy 21—an extra chromosome 21 in a person's cells.

24. The G_1 state of the cell cycle is the phase of cell growth. This is followed by the S stage, in which DNA is copied. G_2 involves the cell preparing for cell division. During mitosis, the nucleus of a cell is divided into two nuclei with each nucleus containing the same number and kinds of chromosomes as the original cell. The cell cycle continues with cytokinesis, the stage during which the cytoplasm divides.

25. Animal cells lack cell walls. The cytoplasm is divided when a belt of protein threads pinches the cell in half. In plant cells, the Golgi apparatus forms vesicles that fuse in a line along the center of the cell and form a cell plate. A new cell wall then forms on each side of the cell plate.

CHAPTER 7
Meiosis and Sexual Reproduction

TRUE/FALSE

1. F
2. T
3. T
4. T
5. F

MULTIPLE CHOICE

6. a
7. d
8. a
9. b
10. c
11. c
12. d
13. b
14. b

COMPLETION

15. gametes
16. anaphase II
17. meiosis, mitosis
18. diploid cells, chromosomes or DNA
19. Genetic diversity
20. meiosis
21. sexual reproduction, genetic recombination
22. diploid

ESSAY

23. Crossing-over results in the exchange of corresponding segments of DNA between homologous chromosomes. This results in genetic recombination.

24. In independent assortment in humans, each of the 23 pairs of chromosomes separates independently. Thus, about 8 million gametes with different gene combinations can be produced from one original cell. DNA is exchanged during crossing-over. This results in chromosomes in which the two chromatids no longer have identical genetic material.

25. Sexual reproduction creates genetic recombinations that may change the characteristics of the organisms. If there has been no change in environmental conditions that would require an adaptation by the organism, the new combinations of genes might harm the individual's ability to survive.

CHAPTER 8
Mendel and Heredity

TRUE/FALSE

1. T
2. F
3. T
4. T

MULTIPLE CHOICE

5. a
6. c
7. a
8. b
9. a
10. a
11. d
12. b
13. a
14. c
15. d

COMPLETION

16. alleles or genes
17. F$_2$
18. alleles
19. probability
20. mutations
21. sex-linked

ESSAY

22. Some traits are controlled by several genes, rather than by only one.

23. Most sex-linked characteristics are carried as alleles on the X chromosome. A male would express a sex-linked recessive trait if he gets the gene for the trait from his mother. He cannot get an X chromosome from his father. A female would have to get the gene for the recessive trait on both of the X chromosomes she receives—the one from her mother and the one from her father.

24. Examples include the changing colors of the arctic fox's fur in response to changes in the season; the darker coloration of the nose, ears, tail, and paws of a Siamese cat as a result of lower body temperature in those areas; and the different colors of hydrangea flowers resulting from different acid levels in the soil.

25. An individual with PKU lacks the enzyme that converts the amino acid phenylalanine into the amino acid tyrosine. The buildup of phenylalanine in the body leads to severe mental retardation.

CHAPTER 9
DNA: The Genetic Material

TRUE/FALSE

1. T
2. F
3. T
4. T

MULTIPLE CHOICE

5. c
6. d
7. d
8. c
9. a
10. d
11. a
12. d
13. b
14. c
15. b

COMPLETION

16. transformation
17. replication
18. DNA polymerase
19. diffraction
20. double helix

ESSAY

21. Hershey and Chase used radioactive labeling to tag bacteriophage DNA with ^{32}P and bacteriophage coat proteins with ^{35}S. They found that the ^{32}P label had been injected inside the bacterial cells and that the ^{35}S label had remained outside the cells. They concluded that the bacteriophages injected the DNA into the host bacterial cells but the protein remained on the outside of the cell.

22. Erwin Chargaff discovered in 1949 that in DNA, the amount of adenine always equals the amount of thymine and the amount of cytosine always equals the amount of guanine. The X-ray diffraction photographs of DNA taken by Wilkins and Franklin in 1952 revealed a tightly coiled helix of two or three nucleotide chains.

23. Enzymes called helicases break the hydrogen bonds that hold the two complementary strands of the DNA double helix together, allowing the helix to unwind. At the replication forks, the points where the double helix separates, a molecule of DNA polymerase attaches and begins to add nucleotides to the exposed bases according to the base-pairing rules. This continues until all of the DNA is copied.

24. DNA polymerases are able to "proofread" the nucleotide sequence along the new DNA strand. The enzymes will backtrack to remove an incorrect nucleotide and replace it with the correct nucleotide.

25. Because bacterial DNA is circular, replication usually occurs using two replication forks that begin at a single origin on the molecule. In humans, DNA is a long strand. Therefore, replication occurs along approximately 100 sections, each with its own replication origin.

CHAPTER 10
How Proteins Are Made

TRUE/FALSE

1. T
2. T

3. T
4. F
5. F

MULTIPLE CHOICE

6. d
7. d
8. d
9. a
10. c
11. b
12. a
13. b
14. c
15. a
16. c

COMPLETION

17. translation
18. anticodons
19. Enhancers
20. genetic disorder

ESSAY

21. A gene's instructions for making a protein are transferred from DNA to mRNA during the process of transcription. In translation, tRNA, rRNA, and ribosomes use the instructions on the mRNA to put together the amino acids that make up the protein.

22. It suggests that all life-forms have a common evolutionary ancestor with a single genetic code.

23. When present in prokaryotic cells, lactose binds to the repressor protein and changes the protein's shape. The repressor prevents RNA polymerase from binding to the promoter. The change in shape releases the repressor. With the blocking effect eliminated, the transcription of genes that code for lactose-metabolizing enzymes proceeds.

24. Introns are long segments of nucleotides in eukaryotic genes with no coding information. After transcription, enzymes remove introns from the mRNA molecule before the mRNA is transcribed.

25. A point mutation is a mutation that changes one or just a few nucleotides in a gene. In a substitution, one nucleotide is replaced with another. Insertions and deletions involve the addition or omission, respectively, of one or more nucleotides.

CHAPTER 11
Gene Technology

TRUE/FALSE

1. T
2. T
3. T
4. T

MULTIPLE CHOICE

5. a
6. d
7. b

8. c
9. a
10. d
11. d
12. b
13. d

COMPLETION

14. genetic engineering
15. DNA fingerprint
16. plasmids
17. clones
18. restriction enzymes
19. Southern blot
20. probes
21. vaccine

ESSAY

22. First, DNA from the organism containing the gene of interest and DNA from the vector, such as a plasmid, are cut with a restriction enzyme. Then the DNA fragments from the two sources are combined. The recombinant DNA is inserted into bacteria. The recipient bacterial cells are cloned. Finally, the bacterial cells are screened to identify and isolate those specific bacterial cells that contain the transferred gene and that are producing the protein coded for by the gene.

23. DNA fingerprints are used in paternity cases, in forensics, and in the identification of the genes that cause genetic disorders.

24. Tumor necrosis factor (TNF) is normally secreted by certain white blood cells in humans. After TNF is added to cancer-seeking white blood cells, the modified white blood cells are able to both find and destroy cancer cells.

25. Gel electrophoresis uses an electrical field within a gel to separate DNA fragments by their size and charge, allowing the fragments to be identified.

CHAPTER 12
History of Life on Earth

TRUE/FALSE

1. F
2. F
3. T
4. F
5. T

MULTIPLE CHOICE

6. d
7. d
8. b
9. b
10. d
11. c
12. a
13. b
14. c
15. c
16. d

COMPLETION

17. Protists
18. Permian
19. ultraviolet
20. Amphibians
21. fishes
22. Fungi, Plantae, Animalia
23. Insects, wings

ESSAY

24. (1) Hydrogen-containing gases are trapped in underwater bubbles. (2) The gases, protected from ultraviolet radiation, react to produce simple organic molecules. (3) The bubbles rise and burst at the surface, releasing the organic molecules. (4) Wind carries the molecules, which react further when exposed to ultraviolet radiation and lightning. (5) Rain sends the new, more complex organic molecules into the ocean. Another cycle begins.

25. The organisms that survived the mass extinctions found themselves in a world of opportunity—an Earth full of food and space.

CHAPTER 13
The Theory of Evolution

TRUE/FALSE

1. T
2. F
3. T
4. T

MULTIPLE CHOICE

5. b
6. c
7. b
8. b
9. c
10. c
11. a
12. b
13. d
14. c
15. a
16. c

COMPLETION

17. environment
18. vestigial
19. ancestor
20. survive
21. fossils, preserved, mineralized
22. natural selection
23. descent, modification

ESSAY

24. A small percentage of the insects exposed to the insecticides were not affected by the insecticide. These insects survived and produced offspring that were also resistant to the insecticide.

25. According to Darwin's theory, those organisms with traits that are best suited to the environment are more likely to survive and reproduce than those that do not have such traits.

CHAPTER 14
Human Evolution

TRUE/FALSE

1. F
2. T
3. F
4. T
5. T

MULTIPLE CHOICE

6. d
7. d
8. c
9. c
10. b
11. c
12. d
13. d
14. b
15. d
16. d

COMPLETION

17. grasping
18. binocular
19. prosimians
20. mitochondrial
21. brains, tools
22. *Homo erectus*

ESSAY

23. Some scientists argue that independent *Homo erectus* groups living in Africa, Europe, and Asia interbred and thus *Homo sapiens* arose simultaneously all over the globe. Most scientists argue that *Homo sapiens* appeared in Africa and then migrated to Europe and Asia, replacing *Homo erectus* as they migrated.

24. At 4.4 million years old, it is the oldest hominid fossil yet discovered. Because it is more apelike than australopithecine, it was assigned to a new group, *Ardipithecus*.

25. In primates, increased brain size has resulted in greater capacity for higher thought processes, such as memory, intelligence, and communication. Having better-developed, higher thought processes enables an animal to survive better in the environment in which it lives.

CHAPTER 15
Classification of Organisms

TRUE/FALSE

1. F
2. F
3. T
4. F
5. T

MULTIPLE CHOICE

6. c
7. b
8. d
9. a

10. b
11. d
12. a
13. d
14. c

COMPLETION

15. evolutionary systematics
16. genus, species
17. reproductive
18. least, most
19. phylogeny
20. species, genus
21. asexually
22. Cladistics

ESSAY

23. If a scientist does not know anything about an organism other than what it looks like and what features it has, cladistics is a better starting point for classification. If a scientist can relate the organism's characteristics to those of other, similar organisms and thus possibly understand the importance of those features to the organism's ability to survive and function, then evolutionary systematics is more applicable.

24. In evolutionary systematics, the levels of biological classification take into account the significance of an organism's evolutionary adaptations and the impact of these adaptations on the organism's survival and success. The relationships identified through evolutionary systematics reflect a more complete picture of an organism's characteristics. Cladistics only identifies whether a group of organisms shares derived traits.

25. Several reproductive barriers are incomplete in this example. The geographical barrier breaks down where the two ranges meet. The two species also share some physical and behavioral similarities.

CHAPTER 16
Populations

TRUE/FALSE

1. F
2. F
3. T
4. F
5. T
6. F

MULTIPLE CHOICE

7. c
8. d
9. b
10. d
11. c
12. c
13. d
14. b
15. b
16. c
17. c
18. d

COMPLETION

19. carrying capacity
20. r-strategists
21. K-strategists
22. Stabilizing
23. Genetic uniformity
24. evolutionary forces

ESSAY

25. Natural selection favors individuals possessing traits that help them survive. These individuals are more likely to produce offspring that may inherit their parents' favorable traits. Over time the number of individuals with favorable traits increases.

CHAPTER 17
Ecosystems

TRUE/FALSE

1. F
2. T
3. F
4. F
5. T

MULTIPLE CHOICE

6. a
7. b
8. d
9. b
10. b
11. c
12. d
13. d
14. a
15. d

COMPLETION

16. one-tenth
17. detritivores
18. sulfur, calcium, phosphorus (also accept hydrogen and oxygen [because, among other reasons, water is recycled])
19. heat
20. energy, food web
21. transpiration
22. nitrogen gas, nitrogen fixation

ESSAY

23. Animals are on higher trophic levels than plants. It takes several pounds of grain to produce 1 lb of meat.

24. Decomposers release matter from waste materials and dead organisms. Were it not for the action of decomposers, Earth would eventually run out of essential matter that organisms need, such as carbon and nitrogen.

25. Photosynthetic organisms use carbon dioxide dissolved in the air to build the organic molecules needed to carry out their life processes. The organic molecules can also be used by other organisms as a source of energy and materials, such as minerals.

CHAPTER 18
Biological Communities

TRUE/FALSE
1. F
2. T
3. F
4. F
5. T

MULTIPLE CHOICE
6. c
7. a
8. d
9. d
10. a
11. d
12. b
13. d
14. c
15. c
16. b
17. b

COMPLETION
18. tropical rain forest
19. commensalism
20. Realized niches
21. competitive exclusion
22. taiga
23. littoral zone

ESSAY
24. No two species can have the exact same niche. The principle of competitive exclusion states that if two species are competing for the same resources, the species that uses the resources more efficiently will eventually eliminate the other.
25. Marshes and wetlands are intermediate habitats between the open water and the land.

CHAPTER 19
Human Impact on the Environment

TRUE/FALSE
1. T
2. F
3. T
4. F
5. T

MULTIPLE CHOICE
6. d
7. b
8. d
9. d
10. b
11. b
12. d
13. c
14. a
15. d

COMPLETION
16. ultraviolet

17. habitat
18. support
19. death
20. pollution

ESSAY
21. Before its use was restricted, DDT was introduced liberally into the environment as an insecticide. The DDT passed from ground water and soil to plants and small animals and then to animals at higher trophic levels, becoming more concentrated at each level.
22. (1) Assess the problem by collecting data.
    (2) Perform a risk analysis to evaluate the various possible courses of action.
    (3) Educate the public about the most feasible course of action and its cost and expected results.
    (4) Implement a solution through political action.
    (5) Follow through on any action taken, to verify that the problem is being effectively addressed and solved.
23. Acid rain began to be produced when smokestacks that released sulfur-rich smoke into the atmosphere were built. Such sources of sulfur smoke did not exist 200 years ago.
24. We reduce our chances to learn about these species; many species offer possible benefits to humans. Many plant and animal species are used to develop improved food sources, medicines, or cures for diseases.
25. The chemicals were washed into the river in Switzerland, then they flowed downstream through Germany and the Netherlands and out into the North Sea.

CHAPTER 20
Introduction to the Kingdoms of Life

TRUE/FALSE
1. F
2. F
3. T
4. T

MULTIPLE CHOICE
5. d
6. d
7. d
8. a
9. c
10. a
11. a
12. d
13. d

COMPLETION
14. eubacterium, archaebacterium
15. Animalia
16. differentiation
17. pseudopodia, porous shells
18. colonial organism
19. Zygosporangia, mushrooms, ascocarps
20. structure, function

ESSAY

21. Halophiles are members of the kingdom Archaebacteria that live in very salty places like the Great Salt Lake.

22. cell type, cell construction, body type, and method of obtaining nutrition

23. Nonflowering seed plants produce seeds. Seedless vascular plants, such as ferns, reproduce by means of spores.

24. All vertebrates have an internal skeleton made of bone, a vertebral column that surrounds and protects the spinal cord, and a head containing the skull and brain.

25. As autotrophs, plants are the primary producers in most terrestrial food webs. Plants provide food for humans and other animals. As heterotrophs, animals are primary consumers, secondary consumers, or parasites in most terrestrial food webs.

CHAPTER 21
Viruses and Bacteria

TRUE/FALSE

1. F
2. F
3. T
4. T

MULTIPLE CHOICE

5. d
6. c
7. b
8. d
9. d
10. a
11. d
12. b
13. a
14. b
15. d

COMPLETION

16. heterotrophic
17. lysogenic, lytic
18. nitrification, nitrate
19. Endospores
20. chemoautotrophic
21. lysogenic

ESSAY

22. Although viruses contain DNA and/or RNA, they are not considered living because they do not grow, do not have homeostasis, and do not metabolize. Viruses cause disease in many living organisms and therefore have a major impact on the living world.

23. Antibiotics work by interfering with cellular processes. Since cellular processes do not occur in viruses, antibiotics are not effective against viruses.

24. Bacteria can have two types of cell walls that can be distinguished by means of Gram staining. One group of bacteria is called Gram-negative, and the other group of bacteria is

called Gram-positive. The two groups of bacteria differ in their susceptibility to different antibiotics. Therefore, it is important in medicine to be able to distinguish one group from the other.

25. Bacteria secrete chemicals called toxins into their environment. These toxins, which are poisonous to eukaryotic cells, can be secreted into the body of an infected person or into a food in which bacteria are growing. Humans who eat food contaminated with bacterial toxins can become ill.

CHAPTER 22
Protists

TRUE/FALSE

1. F
2. T
3. F
4. T
5. F

MULTIPLE CHOICE

6. d
7. d
8. d
9. d
10. b
11. b
12. c
13. c
14. d
15. c

COMPLETION

16. multicellularity
17. bilateral
18. plankton, photosynthesizers
19. pseudopodia, amoeba
20. flagellum, flagellate
21. cilia, ciliate

ESSAY

22. Possible answers include the following: amebic dysentery through contaminated food or water, giardiasis through contaminated food or water, African sleeping sickness through the bite of an infected tsetse fly, and toxoplasmosis through contact with infected cats or improperly cooked meat.

23. In the second stage of the life cycle of *Plasmodium*, merozoites infect the host's red blood cells and divide rapidly. In about 48 hours, the blood cells rupture, releasing more merozoites and toxic substances into the host's body and initiating a cycle of chills and fever. The cycle repeats itself every 48 hours as new blood cells are infected.

24. (1) quinine and its derivatives, chloroquine and primaquine; (2) spraying insecticides; (3) introducing animals that will eat mosquito larvae, such as mosquito fish

25. Protists are the single largest group of photosynthesizers on Earth; they produce oxygen and organic matter; and they help recycle

nitrogen, carbon, and phosphorus. Protists also cause serious diseases in humans and livestock. The cost of treating infected livestock is passed on to consumers.

CHAPTER 23
Fungi

TRUE/FALSE

1. F
2. F
3. F
4. T
5. T

MULTIPLE CHOICE

6. d
7. b
8. d
9. b
10. a
11. d
12. a
13. b
14. c
15. d

COMPLETION

16. decomposing
17. basidiomycetes
18. spore
19. ascus
20. mycelium, hyphae
21. yeasts
22. zygosporangia, asci, basidia

ESSAY

23. A mycorrhiza is a relationship between a fungus and the roots of vascular plants. The fungal hyphae can either penetrate the outer cells of the root or wrap around the root. The fungus transfers minerals from the soil to the plant. The plant provides the fungus with carbohydrates. A lichen is a relationship between a fungus and a photosynthetic partner such as an alga, a cyanobacterium, or both. The fungus, usually an ascomycete, protects the photosynthetic partner and provides it with mineral nutrients. The photosynthetic partner provides the fungus with carbohydrates.

24. The mycelium of a fungus can be made of many meters of individual hyphae. This creates a high surface-area-to-volume ratio, which makes a fungus well suited for absorbing food from the environment.

25. Fossil evidence indicates that the earliest land plants often had mycorrhizae. The soil at that time lacked organic matter. Plants with mycorrhizae are particularly successful in infertile soil.

CHAPTER 24
Introduction to Plants

TRUE/FALSE

1. F
2. F
3. T
4. T
5. T

MULTIPLE CHOICE

6. a
7. b
8. d
9. d
10. c
11. d
12. d
13. a
14. c
15. d

COMPLETION

16. stomata
17. protect, nourish
18. gametophytes
19. starch, legumes
20. wing, dispersal
21. embryo
22. stored food

ESSAY

23. Possible answers include the following: Phylum Bryophyta, the mosses, contains plants with large, green gametophytes and smaller, nongreen sporophytes. Phylum Hepatophyta, the liverworts, contains plants with large, green gametophytes, which sometimes resemble the lobes of a liver, and very small sporophytes. Phylum Anthocerophyta, the hornworts, contains plants that have green gametophytes and smaller, hornlike sporophytes. Phylum Pterophyta, the ferns, contains plants with large, green sporophytes that have roots, stems, and leaves, and small green gametophytes. Phylum Lycophyta, the club mosses, contains plants with large, green sporophytes that have roots, stems, and leaves, and they form cones containing spores. Phylum Sphenophyta, the horsetails, contains plants with large, green sporophytes that have roots, stems, and leaves, and they produce cones containing spores. Phylum Psilotophyta, the whisk ferns, contains plants with large, green sporophytes that have stems but no roots or leaves, and they produce spores in sporangia. Phylum Coniferophyta, the conifers, contains plants with large, green vascular sporophytes that produce seeds in cones. Phylum Cycadophyta, the cycads, contains plants with large, green vascular sporophytes that produce seeds in cones. Phylum Ginkgophyta, the ginkgos, contains plants with large, green vascular sporophytes that produce seeds that are not enclosed in cones. Phylum Gnetophyta, the gnetophytes, contains plants with large, green, vascular

sporophytes that produce cones containing seeds. Phylum Anthophyta, the angiosperms, contains plants with large, green vascular sporophytes that produce flowers and fruits, which contain seeds.

24. Some flowers, such as roses, have brightly colored petals or strong scents. These characteristics attract insects and other animals that carry pollen and therefore increase the likelihood of cross-pollination. Other flowers, such as garden peas, are adapted for self-pollination. The flowers of oaks and grasses have small greenish flowers that are adapted for wind pollination.

25. Solutions made by soaking the bark of willow trees yielded a substance that was used to cure aches and pains. That substance was later identified as the chemical salicin. Acetylsalicylic acid, a derivative of salicin, was first sold under the name *aspirin* in 1899.

CHAPTER 25
Plant Reproduction

MULTIPLE CHOICE
1. d
2. a
3. c
4. b
5. d
6. c
7. b
8. c
9. b
10. a
11. d
12. a
13. c
14. b

COMPLETION
15. gametophytes, pistil
16. pollen grains, ovule, pollen tube
17. cotyledon
18. sepals, petals, stamens, pistil
19. seed, sporophyte
20. seeds, vegetative parts

ESSAY
21. The diploid sporophyte produces haploid spores by meiosis. The spores fall to the ground and grow into haploid gametophytes, which produce gametes—sperm and eggs—by mitosis. When water covers the gametophytes, sperm can swim to the archegonia and fertilize the eggs inside of them. The zygotes, or fertilized eggs, grow into new sporophytes.

22. At the time of pollination, the scales of a female cone are open, exposing the ovules. When a pollen grain lands near an ovule, a slender pollen tube grows out of the pollen grain and into the ovule. The sperm moves through the pollen tube and enters the ovule to reach the egg. The pollen tube provides a way for the sperm to reach the egg without having to swim through water.

23. The pollen tube links a pollen grain with an ovule. Each grain contains two sperm that travel through the tube to the ovule. One sperm fuses with the egg and forms the zygote. The other sperm fuses with two other haploid nuclei and develops into the endosperm. The zygote and the endosperm develop into a seed, which grows into a new sporophyte.

24. Many plants produce structures that can grow into new plants. Some examples are bulbs, corms, rhizomes, and tubers, which are modified stems. Pieces of roots, stems, and leaves may also grow into new plants.

25. Plantlets are tiny new plants that develop by vegetative reproduction in notches along the leaf margins of the kalanchoë. When a plantlet falls to the ground, it grows into a plant that is identical to the parent plant.

CHAPTER 26
Plant Structure and Function

TRUE/FALSE
1. T
2. F
3. T
4. T
5. T
6. F

MULTIPLE CHOICE
7. c
8. a
9. c
10. d
11. d
12. c
13. d
14. b
15. d

COMPLETION
16. modified leaves
17. xylem
18. nutrient storage, vegetative reproduction
19. mesophyll, ground
20. stomata, transpiration
21. xylem, phloem, ring
22. spongy layer, air spaces

ESSAY
23. When two guard cells take in water, they increase in length, but not diameter. This causes the cells to bend away from each other, opening the stoma. When water leaves the guard cells, they shorten and move closer to each other, closing the stoma.

24. Organic compounds move from a source, where they are made or stored, to a sink, where they are used. Leaves and roots are sources. Roots, stems, and developing fruits are sinks.

25. Sugar from a source enters the phloem by active transport. This increases the sugar concentration in the phloem and causes water

to enter the phloem cells from the xylem by osmosis. Pressure builds up inside the phloem and forces the sugar through the phloem. Sugar then moves from the phloem into a sink by active transport.

CHAPTER 27
Plant Growth and Development

TRUE/FALSE
1. F
2. T
3. F
4. T
5. T

MULTIPLE CHOICE
6. d
7. d
8. a
9. b
10. c
11. c
12. c
13. a
14. b
15. a

COMPLETION
16. germination
17. meristems
18. differentiation
19. Apical, vascular, cork
20. hormones
21. auxin
22. dormancy
23. continuous, reversible

ESSAY
24. One meristem, called the vascular cambium, develops between the primary xylem and phloem in the vascular bundles of a young woody stem. The vascular cambium produces new layers of secondary xylem and phloem each year. A second meristem, the cork cambium, forms when the epidermis is stretched and broken. Cork cambium produces cork cells, which become part of the bark.
25. The stems of wheat plants, called culms, are hollow and jointed. There may be as many as 100 culms in a mature plant. The roots are fibrous and are composed mainly of adventitious roots. About 85 percent of a wheat kernel (grain) is starchy endosperm. The bran, or outer covering, consists of the ovary wall, seed coat, and aleurone layer. About 12 percent of the kernel is bran. The embryo, or wheat germ, is less than 3 percent of the kernel.

CHAPTER 28
Introduction to Animals

TRUE/FALSE
1. T
2. T
3. T
4. F
5. F

MULTIPLE CHOICE
6. a
7. d
8. d
9. c
10. d
11. b
12. c
13. a
14. b
15. a

COMPLETION
16. heterotrophs
17. mouth, anus
18. radial symmetry
19. movement
20. cephalization
21. tissue
22. gastrovascular cavity

ESSAY
23. In an open circulatory system, the heart pumps blood through vessels into the body cavity. As the fluid moves across the body's tissues, it supplies them with oxygen and nutrients. The fluid then collects in open spaces within the animal's body and is returned to the heart. In a closed circulatory system, the blood remains inside the vessels and does not directly touch the body's tissues. Oxygen and nutrients diffuse through the walls of the blood vessels.
24. Bilateral symmetry allowed different body parts to become specialized in different ways. One major specialization was cephalization, the development of sensory structures and nerves at the animal's anterior end. Animals with heads are usually mobile and are better at finding food and sensing danger.
25. Digestive enzymes help break down the food particles into pieces that are small enough to move through cell membranes. This permits an animal to eat food items that are larger than its cells.

CHAPTER 29
Simple Invertebrates

TRUE/FALSE
1. T
2. T
3. T
4. F
5. F

MULTIPLE CHOICE

6. d
7. d
8. a
9. d
10. b
11. d
12. b
13. d
14. a
15. b

COMPLETION

16. choanocytes
17. gemmule
18. hermaphrodite
19. tegument
20. proglottids

ESSAY

21. Cnidocytes are stinging cells located on the tentacles of cnidarians. Cnidocytes contain nematocysts, which are small, harpoonlike structures that may contain deadly toxins or other chemicals. Nematocysts are used for defense and to capture prey.

22. The pseudocoelom contains fluid. This fluid serves as a simple circulatory and gas exchange system, carrying nutrients, oxygen, and carbon dioxide throughout the animal's body. The materials move into and out of cells by diffusion.

23. Medusae are free-floating, jellylike, and often umbrella shaped. Polyps are tubelike and are usually attached to a rock or some other object. A fringe of tentacles surrounds a polyp's mouth, which is located at the free end of the body. Examples include jellyfish (medusa) and sea anemone (polyp).

24. Answers will vary but should include cooking meat thoroughly to kill all larvae it may contain, wearing shoes in areas where animal hosts are commonly found, and wearing protective clothing when wading in waters that may be contaminated with *Schistosoma*.

25. Portuguese man-of-wars are sometimes called jellyfish, but they are colonial hydrozoans. These animals include a gas-filled float that may be a specialized polyp. Tentacles that may be as long as 15 m trail under the water. Specialized polyps and medusae carry out such functions as sexual reproduction, food capture, and feeding.

CHAPTER 30
Mollusks and Annelids

TRUE/FALSE

1. T
2. F
3. F
4. T

MULTIPLE CHOICE

5. a
6. c
7. a
8. b
9. d
10. b
11. c
12. a
13. a
14. c
15. b

COMPLETION

16. trochophore
17. cilia
18. siphons
19. cerebral ganglion
20. septa, setae (or parapodia)

ESSAY

21. The visceral mass is a central section that contains the mollusk's organs. The mantle is a heavy fold of tissue that encloses the visceral mass. The mantle forms the outer layer of the body. The foot is a large muscular region that is used primarily for locomotion.

22. The polychaetes (marine worms) possess parapodia that usually have setae on each body segment. Oligochaetes (primarily earthworms) completely lack parapodia and have only a few setae per segment. Hirudineans (leeches) have neither setae nor parapodia and have suckers at both ends of their bodies.

23. Answers will vary but may include their complex nervous system and complex behaviors, and their ability to be trained to distinguish objects.

24. They draw water into their mantle cavity and then close the mantle quickly. This forces the water to shoot out of the siphon and creates a jet-propulsion effect.

25. Earthworms' tunnels allow air to penetrate the soil, and earthworms' castings (undigested materials) fertilize the soil.

CHAPTER 31
Arthropods

TRUE/FALSE

1. F
2. T
3. F
4. T

MULTIPLE CHOICE

5. c
6. a
7. d
8. d
9. c
10. d
11. d
12. b
13. d
14. b

COMPLETION

15. mandibles
16. head, thorax, abdomen
17. insects
18. pedipalp
19. poison gland
20. Book lungs

ESSAY

21. The grasshopper could not live. It must molt in order to grow.

22. Possible answers include the following: five pairs of walking legs; a protective carapace that covers the fused head and thorax; large pincers called chelipeds; swimmerets used in swimming and in reproduction; flattened, paddlelike appendages called uropods; and possibly a telson, or tail spine.

23. Covering the arthropod body is an exoskeleton, which is thinner and more flexible where joints and appendages are located. Muscles attached to the interior surfaces of the exoskeleton close to the joints pull against the exoskeleton, causing the joint to bend.

24. Answers should include the following: a cephalothorax and abdomen; no antennae; chelicera, which are mouthparts modified into fangs or pincers; pedipalps, which are appendages modified to catch and handle prey; and four pairs of walking legs.

25. The insect thorax is composed of three fused segments, and three pairs of legs are attached to the thorax. Most insects also have two pairs of wings attached to the thorax.

CHAPTER 32

Echinoderms and Invertebrate Chordates

TRUE/FALSE

1. T
2. F
3. T
4. T
5. F

MULTIPLE CHOICE

6. b
7. a
8. a
9. d
10. d
11. b
12. a
13. b
14. b
15. a

COMPLETION

16. backbone
17. second, mouth
18. tube feet
19. bilaterally, radially
20. pharyngeal slits

ESSAY

21. The water-vascular system of sea stars functions in movement (locomotion), feeding, gas exchange, and waste excretion.

22. Protostomes are animals, such as annelids, mollusks, and arthropods, in which the mouth develops from or near the blastopore. Deuterostomes are animals, either echinoderms or chordates, in which the anus develops from or near the blastopore.

23. Echinoderms have an endoskeleton composed of ossicles. These ossicles sometimes fuse together in adulthood. All echinoderms are radially symmetric as adults. Most have five arms radiating from a central point, but the number of arms can vary. Echinoderms have a water-vascular system that is used for movement, feeding, and gas exchange. The echinoderm body cavity functions as a simple circulatory and respiratory system.

24. At some time in their lives, humans have all four of the chordate characteristics—a notochord, a tail extending beyond the anus, pharyngeal slits, and a single, hollow dorsal nerve cord. For humans, three of these characteristics are present only briefly during embryonic development.

25. Cilia beating inside the tunicate cause water to enter the incurrent siphon. The water circulates through the tunicate's body. As the water passes through the pharyngeal slits, food is filtered out and passes into the stomach.

CHAPTER 33

Introduction to Vertebrates

TRUE/FALSE

1. F
2. T
3. T
4. F
5. T
6. T

MULTIPLE CHOICE

7. c
8. d
9. b
10. c
11. d
12. c
13. d
14. c
15. d
16. b

COMPLETION

17. heart
18. dry
19. feathers, breastbone
20. Marsupials

ESSAY

21. Fishes with jaws and teeth were able to grasp prey and hold on to it. Paired fins provided better control of movement in the water.

22. One hypothesis suggests that the impact from a meteorite collision would have thrown massive amounts of material into the atmosphere, blocking out all sunlight for a considerable period of time and creating a prolonged period of cold temperatures worldwide. If most Cretaceous dinosaurs were warm-blooded, as many scientists think, they would not have been able to survive the cold.

23. The Cretaceous extinction eliminated most animal species that were larger than a small dog. Earth's climate was no longer dry, and the reptiles' adaptations to dry climates were no longer an advantage. Mammals rapidly diversified.

24. Coldblooded, or ectothermic, animals have a metabolism that is too slow to produce enough heat to warm their bodies. Ectotherms, like today's living reptiles, must absorb heat from their environment, and their body temperature changes as the temperature of their environment changes. Warmblooded, or endothermic, animals include mammals and birds. These animals maintain a high, constant body temperature by producing heat internally through a faster metabolism.

25. Coastal climates were warm, with a dry season followed by a rainy season. The interior was dry.

CHAPTER 34
Fishes and Amphibians

TRUE/FALSE

1. F
2. F
3. T
4. F
5. T

MULTIPLE CHOICE

6. d
7. a
8. d
9. c
10. d
11. c
12. c
13. a
14. b
15. c
16. b
17. a
18. d

COMPLETION

19. countercurrent flow
20. urostyle, vertebrae
21. metamorphosis
22. pulmonary
23. tympanic membrane

ESSAY

24. Oxygen-poor blood from the body enters the sinus venosus and then the right atrium. Oxygen-rich blood from the lungs enters the left atrium through the pulmonary veins. The blood in both atria enters the ventricle. The blood in the ventricle is pumped to the conus arteriosis and then to the lungs and the body. Although some mixing of the blood occurs, oxygen-rich blood tends to stay on the side of the ventricle that sends blood to the rest of the body. The oxygen-poor blood tends to stay on the side of the ventricle that sends blood toward the lungs.

25. The operculum, or gill cover, permits a bony fish to pump water over the gills, even when the fish is not swimming.

CHAPTER 35
Reptiles and Birds

TRUE/FALSE

1. F
2. T
3. T
4. F

MULTIPLE CHOICE

5. b
6. c
7. d
8. d
9. a
10. c
11. a
12. b
13. d
14. a
15. c
16. b

COMPLETION

17. ectotherms
18. plastron
19. tuataras
20. alveoli, muscles
21. fangs
22. Feathers, body heat, coloration
23. brain, birds

ESSAY

24. Contour feathers cover a bird's body and give an adult bird its shape. Some contour feathers found on the wings and tail are specialized for flight. Contour feathers may also provide protective coloration. Down feathers cover young birds and are found beneath the contour feathers of adults. Both down feathers and contour feathers conserve body heat and provide lift for flight.

25. Pit organs, located between the eyes and nostrils of a rattlesnake, contain tissue that can detect infrared radiation. Pit organs permit the snake to detect the difference between the infrared radiation emitted by prey and

the infrared radiation emitted by the cooler background. Thus, rattlesnakes can hunt in total darkness.

CHAPTER 36
Mammals

TRUE/FALSE
1. F
2. T
3. T
4. F
5. T

MULTIPLE CHOICE
6. b
7. d
8. a
9. b
10. c
11. d
12. a
13. b
14. a
15. d

COMPLETION
16. duckbill platypus, echidnas
17. rumen, pouch (or cecum), microbes
18. tails, propulsion
19. endothermic
20. gestation period
21. pouch (or marsupium)
22. intelligence, reproduction
23. Ungulates

ESSAY
24. The primary function of hair is insulation. Hair may also serve as camouflage or as a defensive signal to other animals. In some mammals, hair serves a sensory function.
25. Monotremes, like reptiles, lay eggs and have a cloaca. In addition, monotreme shoulders and forelimbs resemble those of reptiles.

CHAPTER 37
Animal Behavior

TRUE/FALSE
1. T
2. F
3. F
4. T

MULTIPLE CHOICE
5. c
6. a
7. d
8. b
9. d
10. b
11. d
12. a
13. c
14. c

COMPLETION
15. reasoning
16. territorial behavior
17. natural selection
18. learning
19. habituation
20. genetic (or innate), learned
21. innate, fixed action pattern
22. genetically programmed, learned

ESSAY
23. It ensures that individuals will mate only with members of their own species.
24. The killing of cubs increases the already high death rate of cubs and therefore does not benefit the species. It does, however, benefit the individual male lion who carries out the killing because it ensures that he will father more cubs. Natural selection has shaped this behavior because natural selection favors traits that contribute to the survival and reproduction of individuals, not species.
25. The rat was in a highly controlled situation; it was locked in a box where it accidentally pressed a lever that released food. It wandered around some more before accidentally pressing the lever again. Then it simply learned to press the lever to obtain food. The chimpanzee stacked boxes to obtain a banana hanging overhead *without* using any experimentation or trial-and-error strategies. The chimpanzee analyzed the situation and reasoned the best way to obtain the banana.

CHAPTER 38
Introduction to Body Structure

TRUE/FALSE
1. F
2. T
3. F
4. F

MULTIPLE CHOICE
5. d
6. a
7. b
8. d
9. d
10. b
11. b
12. d
13. d
14. a
15. b
16. c

COMPLETION
17. periosteum
18. sternum (or breastbone)
19. body cavity
20. extensors

ESSAY
21. Myosin and actin filaments lie parallel along the length of a myofibril in units called sarcomeres. The myosin heads touch the adja-

cent actin filaments. When a muscle fiber is stimulated, the myosin heads attach to the actin filaments. The myosin heads bend inward, pulling the actin filaments. As the filaments slide against one another, Z lines move closer together, shortening the sarcomere. The entire muscle fiber contracts.

22. The outermost layer of the skin is the epidermis. This layer is responsible for protection from the environment. Accessory structures, such as hair and nails, are derived from cells of the epidermis.

23. Blood vessels within the periosteum supply nutrients to bone tissue. Within each Haversian canal, smaller blood vessels carry nutrients to individual osteocytes. Because the Haversian canals extend down the length of a bone, nutrients and waste products can be transported to and from osteocytes anywhere within the bone.

24. As infants, our bones are made mostly of cartilage. Throughout the growing years and through adolescence, the cartilage is constantly being replaced by bone. Bones lengthen as more and more bone cells are added. After the age of about 35, not only does the rate of bone formation decrease, but the body's ability to replace bone becomes less efficient.

25. Acne is caused by excessive secretion of sebum by oil glands in the dermis. Proper skin care can usually keep acne in check, but antibiotics may be necessary in some cases. Carcinomas and malignant melanomas both originate in the epidermis. Using effective sunscreens can help protect the skin from harmful UV radiation, as can avoiding overexposure to either natural or artificial UV radiation. Regular self-examination of moles for changes in shape, size, or color is also helpful.

CHAPTER 39
Circulatory and Respiratory Systems

TRUE/FALSE
1. T
2. F
3. T
4. T

MULTIPLE CHOICE
5. d
6. a
7. c
8. d
9. a
10. c
11. c
12. c
13. a
14. b
15. a

COMPLETION
16. atria
17. hypertension
18. hemoglobin
19. air pressure

ESSAY
20. Some white blood cells consume and destroy bacteria and viruses, while others produce antibodies. Antibodies identify and attach to foreign substances and then other cells of the immune system destroy the foreign substances.

21. Carbon dioxide is dissolved in the blood plasma, is attached to hemoglobin molecules, and is carried in the blood as bicarbonate ions.

22. When air is inhaled, it passes through the nose, the pharynx, the larynx, and into the trachea. Air then passes through the bronchi and into the bronchioles and alveoli of the lungs.

23. Arteries must accommodate the force of blood pulses from the heart. To accomplish this, arteries have a three-layered wall composed of endothelium, smooth muscle, and connective tissue. This allows the walls to expand and stretch and then return to their original size with every contraction of the heart. Capillary walls have a thickness of one cell, which allows for the exchange of gases and small food molecules between the blood and body cells. The tight fit of the red blood cells passing through the narrow diameter of capillaries allows oxygen to diffuse from red blood cells to body cells.

24. Possible answers include: nutrients, oxygen, wastes, hormones, and heat.

25. Plasma consists of water, metabolites, wastes, salts, and proteins.

CHAPTER 40
Digestive and Excretory Systems

TRUE/FALSE
1. F
2. T
3. T
4. F

MULTIPLE CHOICE
5. a
6. a
7. c
8. d
9. c
10. c
11. a
12. c
13. a
14. d
15. c
16. d

COMPLETION

17. fats
18. essential
19. food, molecules
20. pancreas (or small intestine)
21. Cellulose

ESSAY

22. First hydrochloric acid in the stomach is used to unfold large proteins into single protein strands. Then pepsin, a digestive enzyme also secreted by the stomach, cuts the single protein strands into smaller chains of amino acids. Digestive enzymes secreted by cells of the pancreas and small intestine complete the digestion of the amino acid chains into amino acids.

23. Exhalation rids the body of carbon dioxide and some water vapor. Excess water is eliminated through the skin as sweat and through the kidneys as urine. Nitrogenous wastes are carried by the bloodstream to the kidneys, where they are removed from the blood and eliminated in urine.

24. The USDA food pyramid recommends 6–11 servings of grains; 3–5 servings of vegetables; 2–4 servings of fruits; 2–3 servings of milk, yogurt, or cheese; and 2–3 servings of meat, beans, eggs, or nuts per day. The pyramid recommends that fats, oils, and sweets be included in the diet only sparingly.

25. In females, the urethra lies in front of the vagina and is only about 2.5 cm (1 in.) long. This short length makes it easier for bacteria and other pathogens to invade the urinary system of females.

CHAPTER 41
The Body's Defenses

TRUE/FALSE

1. T
2. T
3. F

MULTIPLE CHOICE

4. d
5. c
6. d
7. d
8. c
9. d
10. a
11. a
12. a
13. d
14. c

COMPLETION

15. Cytotoxic, pathogens
16. Macrophages
17. helper
18. plasma cells, antibodies
19. Histamine
20. autoimmune
21. Interferon

ESSAY

22. Macrophages engulf the virus and display the viral antigen. Helper T cells bind to the viral antigen, and the macrophages release the protein interleukin-1. Interleukin-1 activates the helper T cells, which release interleukin-2, activating B cells and cytotoxic T cells. The B cells divide and develop into plasma cells, which produce antibodies. The antibodies bind to the viral antigen on the surface of virus-infected cells. Cytotoxic T cells then destroy the infected cells.

23. Possible answers include: kissing, shaking hands, touching open wounds or sores, and having sexual contact.

24. HIV is transmitted through HIV-infected white blood cells present in body fluids. HIV invades and kills helper T cells. Without a sufficient number of helper T cells, B cells and cytotoxic T cells cannot be efficiently activated. This leaves the infected individual susceptible to a variety of pathogens and cancers.

25. The most rapid division of B cells occurs during the time period labeled C because this is the interval during which antibody production increases at the fastest rate.

CHAPTER 42
Nervous System

TRUE/FALSE

1. F
2. T
3. T
4. T

MULTIPLE CHOICE

5. c
6. b
7. a
8. b
9. d
10. b
11. d
12. a
13. c
14. b

COMPLETION

15. dendrites
16. reflex
17. presynaptic, postsynaptic
18. Mechanoreceptors
19. Olfactory
20. temporal

ESSAY

21. Signals are transmitted at a synapse by neurotransmitters. When a nerve impulse reaches the end of an axon, neurotransmitters are released from the presynaptic neuron into the synaptic cleft. The neurotransmitters move across the synapse and bind to receptors on the postsynaptic cell. This either excites or inhibits the postsynaptic cell.

22. Most sensory and motor processing occurs in the outer layer of the cerebrum, called the cerebral cortex. The capacity for learning, memory, perception, and intellectual function resides in the cerebrum.

23. Addiction is a physiological response caused by repeated use of a psychoactive drug. Tolerance is a characteristic of drug addiction in which increasing amounts of the drug are needed to achieve the desired sensation.

24. Sound waves enter the ear canal and cause the eardrum to vibrate. Three small bones in the middle ear—the hammer, anvil, and stirrup—transfer the vibrations to a membrane in the fluid-filled cochlea in the inner ear. The vibrations reach the membrane and stimulate hair cells, which then send nerve impulses to the brain stem via the auditory nerve. There the thalamus relays the information to the temporal lobe of the cerebral cortex, where the auditory information is processed.

25. Cocaine blocks the reuptake of dopamine by the presynaptic neuron. The excess dopamine overstimulates the postsynaptic cell, which thereby decreases the number of dopamine receptors. This causes the postsynaptic cell to become less sensitive, requiring more cocaine for adequate stimulation.

CHAPTER 43

Hormones and the Endocrine System

TRUE/FALSE

1. F
2. T
3. T
4. T

MULTIPLE CHOICE

5. b
6. a
7. d
8. d
9. c
10. d
11. a
12. c
13. d
14. c
15. a

COMPLETION

16. target cells
17. amino-acid-based
18. hypothalamus
19. Steroid
20. Oxytocin

ESSAY

21. Both the endocrine and nervous systems help coordinate the body's activities with chemical messengers. The endocrine system uses slower-acting, longer-lived hormones that are released either into the bloodstream or into the extracellular fluid. The nervous system uses fast-acting, short-lived neurotransmitters that directly stimulate adjacent cells. Some nerve cells can also secrete hormones.

22. Hormones regulate growth, development, behavior, and reproduction; produce, use, and store energy; maintain homeostasis; and react to stimuli from outside the body.

23. Type I diabetes, which usually develops before the age of 20, is a hereditary autoimmune disease that causes low insulin levels. It is treated with daily injections of insulin. Type II diabetes often develops in people over 40 as a consequence of obesity and an inactive lifestyle. People with Type II diabetes have abnormally low numbers of insulin receptors, while the level of insulin in their blood is often higher than normal. It is treated with diet and exercise and sometimes medication other than insulin.

24. The fight-or-flight hormones are epinephrine and norepinephrine. They affect the body by increasing heart rate, blood pressure, blood-sugar level, and blood flow to the heart and lungs.

25. Endocrine glands secrete hormones into the bloodstream or extracellular fluid. Exocrine glands deliver substances through ducts.

CHAPTER 44

Reproduction and Development

TRUE/FALSE

1. F
2. T
3. F
4. T

MULTIPLE CHOICE

5. d
6. d
7. c
8. d
9. c
10. c
11. a
12. d
13. d
14. c
15. a

COMPLETION

16. meiosis
17. prostate gland
18. progesterone
19. zygote
20. implantation

ESSAY

21. A sperm cell consists of a head, a midpiece, and a long tail. Enzymes in the head help a sperm cell penetrate an egg. The head also contains the nucleus, which can fuse with the nucleus of an egg cell. In the midpiece, mitochondria produce ATP and supply the energy that the sperm cell needs to use its tail to propel itself through the reproductive system.

22. During the second and third trimesters, the fetus grows rapidly and its organs become functional.

23. Prior to ovulation, increasing levels of estrogen cause the lining of the uterus to thicken. After ovulation, high levels of both estrogen and progesterone maintain the uterine lining and cause it to thicken more. If pregnancy does not occur, the levels of estrogen and progesterone decrease, causing the lining of the uterus to shed. This marks the end of the menstrual cycle.

24. ovulation; A—ovum; B—empty follicle; C—developing follicle; D—ovary wall

25. FSH, LH, and estrogen